CW01022265

100 Ideas for Primary Teachers:

Maths

Other titles in the 100 Ideas for Primary Teachers series:

100 Ideas for Primary Teachers: Developing Thinking Skills
by Steve Bowkett

100 Ideas for Primary Teachers: Behaviour Management
by Molly Potter

100 Ideas for Primary Teachers: Outstanding Teaching
by Stephen Lockyer

100 Ideas for Primary Teachers: Writing
by Adam Bushnell, Rob Smith and David Waugh

100 Ideas for Primary Teachers: Supporting Children with Dyslexia
by Gavin Reid and Shannon Green

100 Ideas for Primary Teachers: Raising Boys' Achievement
by Gary Wilson

100 Ideas for Primary Teachers: Homework
by Jenna Lucas

100 Ideas for Primary Teachers: Science
by Paul Tyler and Bryony Turford

100 Ideas for Primary Teachers: Literacy
by Rob Smith and Katherine Simpson

100 Ideas for Primary Teachers: Engaging Parents
by Janet Goodall and Kathryn Weston

100 Ideas for Primary Teachers: History
by Clare Horrie and Rachel Hillman

100 Ideas for Primary Teachers: Questioning
by Peter Worley

100 Ideas for Primary Teachers: Supporting Pupils with Autism
by Francine Brower

100 Ideas for Primary Teachers: Supporting Pupils with Social, Emotional and Mental Health Difficulties
by Roy Howarth

100 Ideas for Primary Teachers: Outdoor Learning
by Adam Bushnell and Sc.out.ed

100 Ideas for Primary Teachers:

Maths

Shannen Doherty

BLOOMSBURY EDUCATION
LONDON OXFORD NEW YORK NEW DELHI SYDNEY

BLOOMSBURY EDUCATION

Bloomsbury Publishing Plc

50 Bedford Square, London, WC1B 3DP, UK

29 Earlsfort Terrace, Dublin 2, Ireland

BLOOMSBURY, BLOOMSBURY EDUCATION and the Diana logo are trademarks of Bloomsbury Publishing Plc

First published in Great Britain 2021

A catalogue record for this book is available from the British Library

ISBN: PB: 978-1-4729-8447-0; ePDF: 978-1-4729-8444-9;
ePub: 978-1-4729-8446-3

2 4 6 8 10 9 7 5 3 1 (paperback)

Typeset by Newgen KnowledgeWorks Pvt. Ltd., Chennai, India
Printed and bound in the UK by CPI Group Ltd, CR0 4YY

To find out more about our authors and books visit www.bloomsbury.com and sign up for our newsletters.

Contents

Acknowledgements

I have been warned to keep this short to avoid it sounding like an Oscar acceptance speech...

Thank you to everyone at Bloomsbury for their support, especially Hannah Marston and Cathy Lear. This literally would not have happened without you believing in me.

There is no doubt in my mind that this would not have been possible without my incredible family. Mad Dog, Mamasita and Kayles: you have always pushed me to be my best self and you encouraged me to let my geek flag fly! Thank you all so much.

Thank you to my best friend, Jen Doel. You kept me sane and pushed me to keep going when I was flagging!

To Lynda and Natalie, and everyone else at St John's, thank you for sharing my excitement and cheering me on the whole time.

Thank you to the NCETM, London Thames and London South East Maths Hubs for the work you've done with me over the years! So much of this comes from my professional development with you.

To my little crowd of Twitter pals, whom I absolutely adore. Emma Cate, Amy Forrester, Ian Addison, Ceridwen Eccles, Kate Owbridge, Paul Steenkamp... I could go on! You are all wonderful and having you around has meant the world.

Finally, thank you to the group who are always willing to answer questions, discuss maths at all times of the day or night and reassure me when I need it. I feel so lucky to have found you all and look forward to talking maths and education with you for years to come. This book would not have happened without Lloyd Williams-Jones, Kieran Mackle, Elliot Morgan, Christopher Such, Matt Swain and the person who boosted my confidence along the way, Neil Almond.

Introduction

As primary teachers, we are fortunate to spend time teaching *all* the subjects. This develops our skill sets as educators and keeps our teaching timetables interesting. While there are many positives to working as primary educators, it does mean we have to spend time honing our craft across a range of subjects. With the emphasis on a high-quality and broad curriculum, we run the risk of diluting our individual subject knowledge.

100 Ideas for Primary Teachers: Maths is a guide to open your minds and develop your own mathematical thinking. It provides practical advice and ideas to be used in your classroom at a range of levels. Ideas include: one-off lessons or activities; lessons or parts of lessons that can be woven into your teaching sequence; pedagogical ideas to develop your mathematics teaching; ways to embed strong use of mathematical language to improve written and verbal explanations as well as reasoning; and a variety of ways to use concrete manipulatives and pictorial representations in your lessons.

This book does not give you a 'mastery approach', but it does give you ideas to weave into your ethos of mastery. Mastery is a culture that needs to be developed and embedded over time. It is not a special set of questions or tasks and it is not a curriculum that can be bought in. Mastery is the ethos of your teaching and learning. There is no way that mastery can be summed up in 100 neat and tidy ideas, but this book will open your eyes to some of the different ways in which you can approach mathematics in primary schools.

Whether you are a trainee, an early career teacher, someone who hates teaching maths, an experienced teacher taking the mastery plunge or a new subject leader, this book will have something for you. I hope you read this and take something from it, be it a lesson idea, some mathematical terminology you didn't know or a way of teaching a particular topic. Maths in the primary classroom should be a fun and interesting subject to teach. You should be enjoying yourself! These ideas will hopefully either kickstart your journey or reignite your love of maths.

If you ever have any questions or want to know more about an idea, please don't hesitate to contact me on Twitter @MissSDoherty.

How to use this book

This book includes quick, easy and practical ideas for you to dip in and out of to help you deliver effective and engaging maths lessons.

Each idea includes:

- a catchy title, easy to refer to and share with your colleagues
- an interesting quote linked to the idea
- a summary of the idea in bold, making it easy to flick through the book and identify an idea you want to use at a glance
- a step-by-step guide to implementing the idea.

Each idea also includes one or more of the following:

Teaching tip

Practical tips and advice for how and how not to run the activity or put the idea into practice.

Taking it further

Ideas and advice for how to extend the idea or develop it further.

Bonus idea ★

There are 31 bonus ideas in this book that are extra-exciting, extra-original and extra-interesting.

Share how you use these ideas and find out what other practitioners have done using **#100ideas**.

Number and place value

Part 1

Base splat

'Exploring different bases gives pupils a deep understanding of the place value system that underpins most of our maths teaching.'

It is no secret that children with a solid and deep understanding of place value will be more successful mathematicians. This idea uses a fun game to help their understanding.

Taking it further

Working in other bases is an excellent way to push your more able pupils higher up in the school. When they have mastered place value and you're stuck for what to give them, play Base splat with them and give them problems using different bases.

Bonus idea ★

This game can be played with children of any age; you could use a tens/ones chart or higher, depending on the year group.
To make it harder, they can start adding their cubes to towers in different columns and splatting when different columns have reached the splat number.

You will need a blank place value chart and some cubes to set up this Base splat game. Children should play in pairs to make sure everyone in the class is participating.

Introduce the splat number, which will replace ten as the base number. Any number from 3–9 will work nicely, but let's say seven for now, and explain that the children will be taking it in turns to add one, two or three cubes to make a tower in the column at the right end of the chart. When they have made a tower of the splat number, they need to bang the table and shout, 'Splat!'. Then they need to make an exchange. They should swap the tower for one cube in the column to the left (the next unit up). This shows they can have a maximum of one less than the splat number in each column. You should model this first.

When they have played a few rounds successfully, stop the class and explain that we follow a base ten system. This means that each column is ten times bigger or smaller than its neighbouring columns and that each column can hold a maximum of nine. They can then practise splatting and exchanging when the towers get ten cubes tall.

This explicit and engaging method of teaching the base ten system will secure the children's understanding of how place value works and should mean that teaching columnar addition and subtraction will be far easier later on.

Spot the mistake!

'I find it easier knowing that there is a mistake to find than having to work out the answer myself.'

This idea will open a door to a range of mathematical reasoning questions that you can ask your class. It is particularly helpful to use with skip counting as children often make mistakes when skip counting aloud or in their heads.

Before you can do any 'spot the mistake' questions, the children need to have been taught the concept you are working on. Here the concept is skip counting, but this works for many other concepts. Skip counting is something that children do throughout primary mathematics lessons, whether it's in multiples of 2, 7, 25 or 1,000.

You should give the children a sequence of numbers, such as:

0, 2, 4, 8, 10, 12

They then need to spot and explain the mistake that has been made.

This can be developed on to counting backwards or in higher multiples, such as:

27, 24, 20, 17, 14, 11, 8

125, 150, 175, 190, 225, 250

In each case, your pupils should first work out what the mistake is and then explain how it went wrong. They should be expected to correct the mistake too.

Teaching tip

Model the written explanation in full sentences with the correct vocabulary to give the children a good example of how to explain the mistake.

Bonus idea ★

Use 'spot the mistake' in other areas of maths, such as written calculation methods.

Battle frames

'The ability to visualise a number and know what makes that number is an important skill in primary mathematics.'

There is a reason that we spend so much time on numbers 1–20 lower down in primary school: an awareness and understanding of a number results in a better understanding of more complex concepts later on. This idea helps children to visualise numbers.

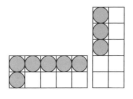

This is a low-input, high-output activity: the gains can be phenomenal.

Each child needs a tens frame and some counters. They compete against their partner to guess each other's chosen number.

First, they need to place a chosen number of counters on their tens frame. To begin with, I suggest having a consistent approach to filling the tens frame such as top row left to right first for a horizontal frame, or left column top to bottom first for a vertical frame. This will mean that your class are better equipped to visualise and guess.

Once this is done, the children take it in turns to ask their partner yes/no questions to guess their partner's number. These could include:

- Is your number an even number?
- Is your number an odd number?
- Is every section of the tens frame full?
- Is the first row/column full?

The winner is the person who guesses the number correctly first! They will begin to work out which questions are more helpful and should become quite quick at guessing.

The children will quickly develop the ability to visualise the numbers on the tens frames.

Guess who?

'The children start coming up with really clever questions to work out what the number is. It really taps into their deeper thinking.'

Children are used to playing guessing games so this idea incorporates that into maths lessons. It encourages them to start thinking creatively about how to guess what the number is.

This versatile idea can be played in pairs, groups or as a whole class. It could be a starter or a filler for those moments where you have a couple of minutes to spare before assembly or at the end of the day. It can be played across primary school; the only part that changes is the size of the number. For example, in Year 4 you could use four-digit numbers whereas in Year 2 you could use two-digit numbers.

To start with, choose a child to go to the front of the class. Hand them a number on a piece of card. They are the only one who knows what that number is. Then, the rest of the class have to ask them closed questions (with yes or no answers) to work out what number is on the card.

At first, the children might ask questions about specific numbers, e.g. 'Is it 345?' But as time goes on, you should encourage them to ask more telling questions, such as:

- Is it even? Is it odd?
- Is it a three-digit number?
- Is the thousands digit even?
- Is the ones digit smaller than five?
- Is there a zero in the number?

The children can take notes to keep track. This will ensure that they are working as a team and are listening to each other's questions. Eventually, they might have enough clues to start guessing.

Taking it further

Give the children a number and ask them to write five clues about it. Then, they swap with a partner and guess each other's numbers.

Crocodile-free comparing

'The crocodile eats the bigger number?'

Comparing numbers should be straightforward. Children should be taught the correct words with helpful models that haven't been dumbed down. The inequality symbols can be taught clearly using this technique.

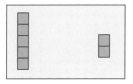

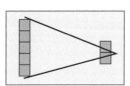

Teaching tip

Ask the children to fill in the gaps using the symbols and the words to ensure they have a good understanding of both.

Teaching the concepts of 'greater than', 'less than' and 'equal to' can seem daunting, especially when you are asking five-year-olds to remember three symbols as well as the corresponding language. However, it is achievable when scaffolded and modelled accurately. The use of gimmicky crocodiles is a thing of the past: children love using proper terminology. There is an expectation that children understand the equals sign (=), so why not greater than (>) and less than (<)?

We can use a simple and adaptable way of introducing the symbols using cubes and whiteboards. Model building a tower of five cubes on one side and a tower of two cubes on the other side. Ask your class, 'Which side has more? How do you know?' Then show them the sentence '5 is _____ 2' and ask them to fill in the gap. When someone says 'more than', introduce the term 'greater than' and ask them to repeat '5 is greater than 2'.

Then, model drawing the greater than symbol over the cubes and explain that sometimes we are lazy in maths so we use symbols instead of words. This symbol means greater than. Explain that '5 > 2' is read as '5 is greater than 2'.

Model more examples of this using different objects such as counters or pencils. Use the same method to introduce 'less than' – and also 'equal to'.

Number line zooming

'I found putting numbers on number lines quite tricky before we spent some time zooming in and out of them.'

A common issue in primary maths is accurately placing numbers on a number line, often due to a lack of focus on subitising and estimating early on. Improving number line work takes dedicated and regular lesson time: here's a 'zooming' idea to help with this.

Starting with a number line from 0–10, ask the children to find the halfway mark. Children should know that half of ten is five and most will be able to make the link between this and the halfway mark on the number line. Now, 'zoom out' to a number line from 0–20. Ask your class questions: Where is the halfway mark this time? What is it? How do we know?

Next, ask them, 'Earlier on, we found five and put it halfway between zero and ten. Can we find five on this number line?' This should be a relatively simple ask. Now the number line should have 0, 5, 10 and 20 labelled.

Then, we will be 'zooming in' to 10–20 on this number line. What is the halfway mark here? How do we know? Once 15 has been labelled, zoom back out and show the whole number line. Ask them where other numbers would go, such as 3 and 13 or 7 and 17. It is vital that children see the relationship between 0–10 and 10–20.

Show the children a new number line from 5–15. Ask them to find the halfway mark and label it. This should be a good indicator of how their number sense has progressed.

Continue to show them different number lines, such as lines up to 30, 50 or 100. Focus on that halfway point each time. Constant questioning is important to secure their understanding.

Teaching tip

Give the children a blank paper number line and reinforce the idea of halfway by asking them to fold their number line in half each time.

Bonus idea

Print three number lines (0–20, 0–30 and 0–50) and ask the children to find 15 on all three. They should see that 15 sits in different places on all three number lines. You could do this with three- or four-digit numbers too.

What's my number?

'Following the clues makes me feel like a maths detective! It also helps me with my understanding of the place value columns.'

Place value underpins most of the maths we teach in primary school. A solid understanding of place value unlocks the maths behind the four operations, as well as many other concepts. Activities like this one mean the children are engaged and are developing their understanding more than they would be if they were completing a stream of questions.

Teaching tip

There will always be children who manage to solve a problem quickly, so a follow-up question of 'How many solutions are there?' will get them thinking and keep them busy.

The class are going to become maths detectives! Write a set of clues on an envelope. These clues will lead them to the number inside the envelope, while also testing their understanding of place value and number. The number inside could be as small as a two-digit number or as large as a seven-digit number, so this idea can be used across different year groups.

- I am thinking of a five-digit number.
- One of the digits is a zero.
- The number is even.
- The tens digit is twice the thousands digit.
- The hundreds digit is three more than the ones digit.
- The ten-thousands digit is odd.
- The digit total is 19.

It is worth giving your class five minutes to read and process the problem and decide how they want to approach it. With any problem-solving activity, it is important to discuss strategies and methods along the way. You might want to model a variation of this problem so the children have a worked example before they attempt to solve it independently.

Rounding rules

'I absolutely hated teaching rounding before I spent a lesson looking at the rules and creating generalisations with the children.'

Rounding is a concept that will help in primary maths, secondary maths and in adult life, so it deserves more time and attention. This idea covers a way to teach it and ensures the children truly understand rounding, rather than it being unreachable.

Lots of teachers will rely on catchy rhymes or gimmicks to teach rules in maths. One of the most popular is 'Five to nine – climb the vine. Zero to four – hit the floor'; children might remember this, but do they truly understand the maths they are doing? Spending time on a concept by unpicking the 'why' behind it will garner the best results and best understanding.

An underused approach in primary maths classrooms is making generalisations. There are rules and patterns throughout mathematics that can be explored in maths lessons, rather than just taught in the abstract. This activity ensures that children spend time thinking about why we round numbers up and down.

Give each child a tens frame in pairs and ask them to go through the numbers 1–9 by placing each number of counters onto the frame. Ask them: 'Is ___ closer to zero or ten? How do you know?'

Of course, when they get to five they will be stuck as it is halfway. This is where we introduce the idea that sometimes in maths we need to agree a rule.

This discussion won't teach them how to round but it will generate a discussion around the rules of rounding, which will mean the children have this in their heads before they attempt rounding to the nearest ten, hundred or thousand.

Teaching tip

When you move on to rounding to the nearest ten, use the stem sentence '___ has a ___ in the ones column so it rounds ___ to ___' to give your pupils a good starting point when explaining their thinking.

Visualise 100 square

'After a while, I could see the number square in my head and knew exactly how to move around it!'

Using a 100 square improves children's ability to see what is happening to numbers when they operate with them, opening the door to mental calculation.

Teaching tip

Print and laminate the 100 squares and ask the children to use whiteboard pens to write on them, so they can be reused later on.

To start with, each child will need a 100 square in front of them. Give the children a starting number, say 27, and then give them instructions such as 'add ten' or 'move three rows down', asking them to follow along. At the end, ask the children to write their end number on a whiteboard and have a look at who is right and who has gone wrong. Then, model the route to show the children the correct version.

1	2	3	4	5	6	7	8	9	10
11	12	13	14	15	16	17	18	19	20
21	22	23	24	25	26	27	28	29	30
31	32	33	34	35	36	37	38	39	40
41	42	43	44	45	46	47	48	49	50
51	52	53	54	55	56	57	58	59	60
61	62	63	64	65	66	67	68	69	70
71	72	73	74	75	76	77	78	79	80
81	82	83	84	85	86	87	88	89	90
91	92	93	94	95	96	97	98	99	100

You could do this at the start of each maths lesson or to settle your class after a break.

Once the children are used to the 100 square, ask them to close their eyes and picture it in their heads instead.

Follow the same process of starting with a number and giving the class instructions to follow. The skill of visualisation is vital later on when approaching more complex concepts.

Reverse 100 square

'Seeing the numbers getting bigger as they get higher made so much more sense to me, especially when I was adding and subtracting ten.'

A reverse hundred square is an unusual way of displaying the numbers 1–100. Ordinarily, the 100 square starts at 1 on the top left and ends at 100 on the bottom right. This idea shows why reversing that order could be beneficial.

A regular 100 square is a model children are often familiar with from board games. However, it doesn't always help children with the size of numbers.

Teaching tip

Introducing the reverse hundred square early on in primary school means the children become accustomed to using it.

91	92	93	94	95	96	97	98	99	100
81	82	83	84	85	86	87	88	89	90
71	72	73	74	75	76	77	78	79	80
61	62	63	64	65	66	67	68	69	70
51	52	53	54	55	56	57	58	59	60
41	42	43	44	45	46	47	48	49	50
31	32	33	34	35	36	37	38	39	40
21	22	23	24	25	26	27	28	29	30
11	12	13	14	15	16	17	18	19	20
1	2	3	4	5	6	7	8	9	10

We use the words 'more', 'greater', 'bigger' and 'higher' when we talk about increasing numbers. A reverse 100 square shows those numbers getting bigger as they get higher. The underlying meaning is that as the rows get higher, so do the numbers. It might seem like a small change, but it is one that could help early on.

Using a reverse hundred square to add or subtract multiples of ten will make it clearer that when you add tens, the numbers get higher and when you subtract tens, the numbers get lower.

Zero pairs

'This is the most effective representation of calculating with negative numbers that I have ever seen.'

Using double-sided counters is an excellent method for showing zero pairs when adding positive and negative numbers.

Teaching tip

Move the children on to drawing out the positive and negative counters in their books and crossing out the zero pairs.

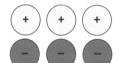

Before introducing this idea, you must ensure that you have covered what negative numbers are and that your class is confident in this area.

You'll need double-sided counters like this to represent positive and negative numbers. One side is positive while the other is negative. Start by showing five positive counters and ask the class what number is represented. Add one more counter and ask them what number is shown now.

Now show five negative counters and ask the class what number is shown. What happens if we add one more counter? This now represents negative six or -6, which is smaller than -5.

Once the class are confident move on to the additive inverse. This is where you add a number to its corresponding negative value, e.g. 3 + (-3), and get 0. We call these zero pairs.

Once your pupils are comfortable with the idea of zero pairs, use them to make calculations such as '-4 + 7' more accessible. Model how to pair the positive and negative counters and see what is left. We can see for example that -4 + 7 = 3, because 3 counters are left without a pair.

Gattegno chart

'A Gattegno chart is vital for teaching place value and powers of ten. I could not teach without it.'

A Gattegno chart is a great tool for teaching place value and exposing our pupils to the patterns in our number system. It has a better structure to it than a standard place value chart and makes the connections between numbers far more explicit.

1,000	2,000	3,000	4,000	5,000	6,000	7,000	8,000	9,000
100	200	300	400	500	600	700	800	900
10	20	30	40	50	60	70	80	90
1	2	3	4	5	6	7	8	9
0.1	0.2	0.3	0.4	0.5	0.6	0.7	0.8	0.9
0.01	0.02	0.03	0.04	0.05	0.06	0.07	0.08	0.09

To start with, point to the numbers on the ones row and ask the children to chant the numbers out loud as you move along, e.g. 'One, two, three, four...'.

Then, begin to include the tens row. When counting through the 'teen' numbers, it is important to draw attention to the ten in the number. So counting 11 requires you to tap ten and then tap one. Counting 12 requires you to tap ten and then tap two. Continue this as you count through the twenties, thirties, etc. It breaks down the numbers for the children so they are constantly exposed to the place value of it all.

The Gattegno chart is a brilliant tool to show the place value of numbers. If you are looking at partitioning a two-digit number into tens and ones, a Gattegno chart shows the structure of the number brilliantly. For example, if you take 42, tap 40 and then 2 to show that 42 is made up of 40 (or four tens) and 2. The same can be done for three- and four-digit numbers or decimals.

Bonus idea ★

Use the Gattegno chart to show what happens when we multiply and divide by 10, 100 and 1,000. You can start with a single-digit number and show the class how that number changes when it is multiplied or divided.

IDEA 13

Roman numerals

'I avoided teaching Roman numerals – they never made sense to me!'

This idea explores how our Arabic numerals relate to Roman numerals. It looks at how breaking down numbers based on place value can help with Roman numeral conversion.

Taking it further

Provide the class with calculations in Roman numerals, such as CLXXXII – CXVIII, and ask them to give their answers in both Roman and Arabic numerals.

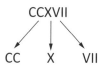

Revise the value of each Roman numeral. Display them on a board one by one or refer to a Roman numeral poster on a working wall. Remind the children of the rules: you can't repeat a letter more than three times; there is no zero; when smaller numerals appear after larger or equal numerals they are added; and when smaller numerals appear before larger numerals they are subtracted.

The children need to see the relevance of place value to Roman numerals. Show them a number written in Roman numerals such as CCXVII and partition it into hundreds, tens and ones.

We know that C = 100, X = 10, V = 5 and I = 1. So CC = 200; X = 10; and VII = 7. We have 200 + 10 + 7, which is 217.

Go through other examples using 'I do, we do, you do' (page 44), breaking it down each time.

Now provide your pupils with an example where the place value is made clear, either through place value counters or dienes, e.g.:

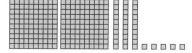

Model how to partition the number shown and then convert it into Roman numerals. An interesting discussion point is why this method of using dienes will not work for a number such as 19, where there is a subtraction taking place (19 = XIX = 10 + 10 − 1).

Addition and subtraction

Part 2

Addition structures

'Breaking addition down into these structures has been a revelation.'

Knowing the underlying structures of the maths we are doing is vital to having a good understanding and solving questions. This idea goes through the two structures of addition.

There are two structures to addition: aggregation and augmentation.

Aggregation is the bringing together of two parts to make a whole. This is when we talk about the total and 'how much altogether'. The parts of an aggregation addition sentence are called addends and the whole is the sum: addend + addend = sum.

Here are some examples:

> There are three blue cars and seven yellow cars.

Augmentation is an increase of an amount. This is when we start with one amount and it gets bigger by another amount. The parts of an augmentation addition sentence are the augend and the addend, where the augend is the original number and the addend is the amount added: augend + addend = sum.

Here are some examples:

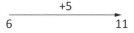

$$+5$$
$$6 \qquad\qquad 11$$

> First, there were two marbles in the bowl. Then, four more marbles were added. How many marbles are in the bowl now?

Subtraction structures

'Knowing the different structures of subtraction meant that my class could approach worded problems confidently and competently.'

Teaching the different structures of subtraction is an important step. The ability to spot what is going on in a problem will enable your class to answer subtraction problems more easily.

There are three subtraction structures: reduction, partition and comparison. We can show these on bar models. Subtraction questions have these parts: the minuend (the original number), the subtrahend (the number subtracted) and the difference (the answer): minuend − subtrahend = difference.

Reduction is when we start with a quantity and reduce it or take some of it away. For example: 'There are 132 cars in a car park and 75 drive away. How many cars are left?'

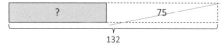

Partition is also known as part–whole. It is when we have the whole and one of the parts, and we need to work out the other part. For example: 'There are 55 people at a party. 34 people are outside, the rest are inside. How many people are inside?'

55	
34	?

Comparison, or finding the difference, is where we have two quantities and we are trying to find the difference between the two. For example: 'There are 10 sweets in 1 jar and 16 in another. How many more sweets in the second jar?'

Bonus idea ★

You can also show the difference model by using cubes. For example, if you were answering the question 'Tom ate nine biscuits and Noah ate three. How many more did Tom eat?' then you would have nine cubes in one bar and three in the other. Lay them next to each other and literally look at what is the same and what is different.

17

Commutativity scales

'Using the number frames made it really easy to learn that you can add numbers in any order!'

This idea relies on balance scales to prove commutativity. The children will have the opportunity to explore numbers and additions to prove that they can add numbers in any order.

Using balance scales is incredibly useful when teaching the concept of the equals sign and also when teaching the commutative law.

Start with a set of scales with the equals symbol stuck on the front to reinforce the relationship between balance and equal.

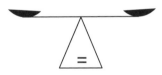

Then, use sticky notes to place two addition sentences onto the two sides of the scales. Ask the children to use different number frames to represent the additions.

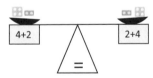

Explain that this concept is the commutative law: numbers can be added together in any order and still produce the same sum.

Your class can experiment with different numbers and different manipulatives such as base ten blocks, cubes, counters or number rods. You could even move some of the children onto using three addends, so they can investigate if that changes the commutativity.

How odd... or even?

'We cannot simply tell our children rules. We need to show them why the rules work.'

There are some rules that we take for granted as teachers. We assume that they are obvious or that someone has already taught these rules. Taking time to investigate and show our class how and why these rules work is vital to ensure our pupils have a deep understanding.

There are many excellent manipulatives out there to use in maths lessons but none expose the oddness and evenness of numbers quite as well as different-coloured number frames. When exploring odd and even numbers early on in primary school, the children can see the even numbers as the number frames with a flat top and the odd numbers as the number frames with an extra 'nobbly bit' on the end. Recapping odd and even numbers before starting this activity is crucial.

Show the children the following three questions. Ask them to use the different number frames to answer the questions and prove that it is always the case.

- What happens when we add an even number to another even number?
- What happens when we add two odd numbers?
- What happens when we add an even number to an odd number?

This activity can be guided by an adult, or the children can be left to their own devices to explore and conjecture before coming back together to discuss what has been discovered. The children can record their findings by drawing out the activity, taking photos of the number frames or writing down the calculations.

Rod bonds

'Number bonds to 10 are part of the essential building blocks for mathematics teaching and learning. Teaching them in a manner that encourages rapid recall can be difficult, so exploring them first is key.'

How often do teachers of Years 5 and 6 bemoan that their children still don't know their number bonds to ten? It is our duty to ensure that this doesn't happen, so we need to find interesting and purposeful activities that go beyond repetition.

Taking it further

Expecting children to memorise all of the number bond facts at once is unreasonable. Give them one to learn and then quiz them on it. Then, start to layer in another fact and continue with the quizzing. Eventually, they will have learnt them all.

Rote learning is the process of learning by memorisation and by repetition out of context. While repetition and re-learning are valuable and necessary strategies in primary maths, there needs to be context for learning to become meaningful. This activity using number rods lays the groundwork for understanding before rapid recall comes into play.

If you have never used these number rods with your class before, you need to dedicate some time to allowing the children to explore them. They should start by just playing with them. They can create pictures or copy a picture you've created. They can make trains from the different rods. They can start learning the different colours. A lovely game to play with them is asking them to have two rods behind their back, e.g. the orange and the brown, and ask them to show you the orange without looking. They begin to get a feel for the different colours way before any numerical value is placed on them.

Place rods around the room at random. Each child (or pair) needs to start with one orange rod. Ask them to find two rods that equal the length of the orange rod when added together. There will be different combinations. Take a solution from one pupil and then ask the class to find all the possible solutions. How many different ways are there?

When the children believe they have found all of the ways, ask them for answers and begin modelling this under the visualiser or on the board. Lay out the rods in a systematic way to show the class that this is how we know if we have all possible solutions. You will end up with something like this:

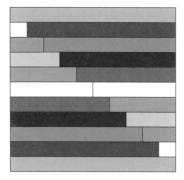

Next, say to the class, 'If the orange rod is 10, what is the value of the other rods?' and give them time to work this out in pairs. When they have done this, label the rods and begin writing down the addition equations by the sides. Now, you can begin the process of chanting and memorising.

Bridge it!

'Showing the maths behind bridging is vital to children's understanding.'

Mental addition and subtraction strategies are essential, not only for primary mathematics but also for life in general. Teaching children specifically how to bridge to ten and what it actually looks like will result in more able mental mathematicians in your classroom.

Teaching tip

This can be done from Year 1 all the way up to Key Stage 2, as it is a strategy that will improve their arithmetic greatly.

Repeating this activity with different numbers will reinforce the process of bridging to ten and ensure the children are more capable of calculating mentally.

Take 7 + 5 as your first example. Show the children 7 on one tens frame and 5 on the other, using two different colour counters to distinguish between the addends. Then, explain to the children that when calculating in our heads, it is easier to get to the nearest ten first and then add the rest. This is because ten is our comfortable base number; we know how to operate with ten. Model moving three counters from the 5 to make the 7 a 10.

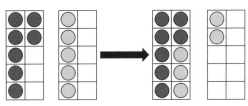

$$7 + 5 = 7 + 3 + 2 = 10 + 2$$

Bonus idea ★

Use a number track or number line as well as the tens frames to show the class a pictorial representation of bridging.

Now, they will see a 10 and a 2, which is more manageable and easier to work with. To move on to bridging mentally, the children will need a strong grasp of number bonds such as 3 + 2 = 5. Once they have a good understanding of adding one-digit numbers, move on to mental additions such as 15 + 8 or even 28 + 14.

Spotting structures

'Exposing children to the structure of the maths they are learning is key to developing fluency and automaticity.'

There is a tendency to rush into using numbers when looking at addition in maths, but we miss out a vital step if we head straight to calculation. This idea introduces the structure of calculation.

Using dienes to expose children to the structure of addition is an extremely beneficial way of opening their eyes to the ins and outs of addition, which should mean that calculating becomes far simpler. Take this question below:

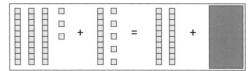

The question can be answered without doing any calculations. Encouraging the children to look at what is the same and what is left over is all that is needed to introduce the concept of addition.

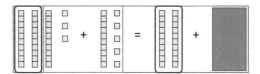

Once the class have spotted the structures within a calculation, the actual calculating becomes far easier. Using the dienes takes all pressure away because they can manipulate these confidently. Then they can look at a question such as '34 + 12 = 22 + ?' and are able to spot the structure in those numbers and how to balance the equation.

Bonus idea ★

Video the process of the children manipulating the dienes and stick a QR code into their books as evidence of their learning.

Counter columns

'Moving the counters and exchanging them made it much easier to do the column method later on!'

Learning formal written methods is something we all remember doing at school, usually just as a procedure. Delving into what the maths looks like in a concrete way will give our pupils an image to visualise when calculating.

Place value counters are an excellent manipulative to have in your classroom, as they are a step on from a more proportional resource, such as base ten blocks. Teaching the column method for addition and subtraction with place value counters first will cement their conceptual understanding of the process.

Take this example of subtraction: 634 − 192.

Place the place value counters onto a grid.

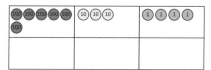

As with the column method, begin with the lowest value column, which is the ones column in this case.

4 ones − 2 ones = 2 ones.

100 100 100 100 100 100	10 10 10	1 1 ⊘ ⊘
		2

Then move on to the tens column.

Here, we are looking at 3 tens − 9 tens. Because 9 tens is larger than 3 tens, we need to exchange. So, we take one hundred and exchange it for 10 tens.

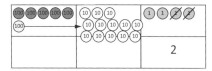

Now we have 13 tens − 9 tens, which is 4 tens.

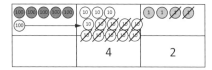

Finally, we need to do 5 hundreds − 1 hundred.

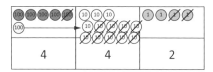

Using place value counters to model and teach the process of exchanging is a valuable activity that will mean your pupils have a deeper understanding of what exchanging is and what it looks like.

Taking it further

For homework, give the children a range of subtraction calculations to do by drawing out place value counters on a grid, as well as using the formal written method.

25

Intelligent practice

'Intelligent practice better draws children's attention to the variation within similar concepts or structures, allowing them to clearly see the boundaries between what they are studying.'

Intelligent practice is the precise designing of activities and practice questions to highlight a concept or structure. Despite more teachers and schools being familiar with the idea of intelligent practice, it is still an underused and valuable method.

Taking it further

Ask the most able pupils to identify what you have done when writing your questions. What little tweaks have you made and why? Then, ask them to write their own set of questions to highlight the same concept or structure.

Often in children's maths books, we see stream after stream of calculation in no particular order. We only have a finite amount of time to teach maths and too much of it is spent on repeating a mechanical activity without any deeper thinking. There is a time and a place for those 'pick 'n' mix' style sets of questions but if we want deep thinkers and able mathematicians in our classrooms, then we need to spend more time thinking about the questions we are setting and the order they face them in.

Here are two sets of questions to consider:

A)	B)
345 – 87	344 – 89
734 – 99	345 – 89
244 – 52	346 – 89
450 – 77	346 – 88
245 – 29	346 – 87
569 – 85	346 – 86

While Set A might be good for assessing a child's understanding of column subtraction, Set B will do that as well as drawing their attention to the effect of adding one to the minuend and then subtracting one from the subtrahend. The variation, or those tiny tweaks along the way in Set B, will expose children to the structure of the maths they are doing, rather than them simply practising a method again and again.

Same difference

'True fluency is far more than recalling number facts; it is the ability to manipulate numbers to make our job easier.'

As adults, we often manipulate numbers in our heads without realising we are doing it. We add, subtract, and change numbers to make them more manageable in order to be more efficient. Teaching children how to do this will make them far more fluent in mathematics than simply memorising a procedure.

Procedural fluency is an important part of mathematics teaching. Children do need to learn and understand methods and procedures to calculate and solve problems. However, with methods and procedures come errors and slips. We need our children to be able to see questions and know how to make them easier to handle or quicker to work out.

For example, a question like 50,000 − 37,214 could result in a range of potential mistakes. Children find a chain of exchanges difficult and are more likely to go wrong. If children have been shown the concept of 'same difference' then they will be able to use a far more efficient method of manipulating 50,000 − 37,214.

Subtracting one from both the minuend (50,000) and the subtrahend (37,214) ensures that the difference remains the same but means that the new calculation − 49,999 − 37,213 − is more straightforward to work out. Spending a lesson or two on this concept, and dropping it in as retrieval practice, will result in more fluent and able mathematicians in your classroom.

Teaching tip

While the example I have shown here uses five-digit numbers, the concept of same difference can be introduced as early as KS1. It is a vital strategy for pupils in Year 2 to have to aid mental calculation.

Questions for challenge

'I love having one of these questions at the end of my work. I feel like I am going behind the scenes of my teacher's brain!'

How often do we get told that we need to challenge our more able pupils? But we also know we can't move them on to a new concept because that isn't mastery. This idea gives you an example of a question you can have 'on hold' for any children who whizz through the work quickly.

Providing suitable challenges for the more able in your maths class does not mean giving them endless worksheets or problem-solving activities. Instead, encourage them to think more deeply about the maths they have been doing. Ask them questions that challenge them to think about why the questions are the way they are.

Where a pupil has worked through a selection of questions or problems quite quickly and you are confident they have learnt what they needed to learn, it is handy to have a selection of questions to draw from to deepen their thinking and move their learning on.

These questions can be applied to a range of topics in maths and are a great way to get your class thinking more deeply about the mathematics that they are doing.

Here are some examples of those questions:

- Why is __ harder than __?
- Why might someone give __ as an answer to question __?
- How have I tried to trick you in question __?
- If I did __, would it become easier or harder?
- Can you create a question that generates the same answer?
- Do you notice a pattern in these questions? What comes next?

Shape solver

'This style of question is a great tool to see how well your pupils are able to make connections and can use this to find the solution!'

Many of the children in your class may appear to have mastered your addition and subtraction objectives. This idea will take them out of their comfort zone and test their understanding.

This idea could have gone in the algebra section but I didn't want it to be missed for those teaching addition and subtraction.

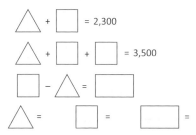

Initially, pupils might want to use a trial and error approach. While this will probably get them the answer, it does not show mastery. A child with a deep understanding will see that in both the top and middle equations, there is a triangle and a square. They know the triangle and square equal 2,300 when added together, so they can work out that the middle line is 2,300 + square = 3,500. Once they have made this connection, they will find the answer very quickly.

Often, parents and children think the highest ability learners are the ones who know all the methods and procedures but, ultimately, they need depth of understanding too. This style of question provides that depth and distinguishes between those who are and are not fluent.

Teaching tip

Before modelling how to approach this question, ensure that you give your class time to process it. That initial settling-in period can be the moment where the lightbulb turns on – you don't want to jump in and take that away from them.

Taking it further

Ask the children to write their own version of this problem. To do this successfully, they will need to understand what should be given and what shouldn't. This is another good way of assessing their understanding.

Multiplication and division

Part 3

Rod ruler repeated addition

'I had never considered using a ruler as a number line before!'

This is an excellent way of introducing repeated addition, using number rods. The ruler is the number line and is a great visual aid to help your pupils with repeated addition without rods.

Take the question 4 x 7. Before the children look at learning how to multiply, they need to see multiplication as repeated addition. So, 4 x 7 = 4 + 4 + 4 + 4 + 4 + 4 + 4.

We can show this using number rods on a centimetre ruler.

After using the rods on a ruler, you can move on to showing it on a number line with the increments marked on.

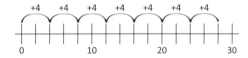

Then, we can move on to an empty number line which the children can label as they go.

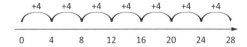

After seeing and experiencing these representations, the pupils should have a good grasp of how addition and multiplication are related, which will result in a deeper understanding of multiplication later on.

Counting stick tables

'This became a go-to maths starter in my classroom and improved their rapid recall tremendously.'

This idea is one that can be used every day in a primary classroom. It will increase pupils' fluency and will get them learning their times tables in no time.

You will need a counting stick and sticky notes for this idea. If you are teaching the three times table, for example, you will need the multiples of three from zero to 36 on sticky notes.

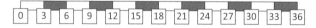

| 0 | 3 | 6 | 9 | 12 | 15 | 18 | 21 | 24 | 27 | 30 | 33 | 36 |

Then, begin chanting through the three times table as a class. Ask the children questions such as, 'What do we start with?' and 'What times table is this?'.

Vary the way you ask the children questions and the way they chant. Alternate between chanting the multiples and asking, 'One times three is... Two times three is...' so they are used to both ways, for example.

After going through the multiples a few times, start taking off the sticky notes as you go so the children begin to rely on their memory.

You can go forwards and backwards to ensure they know the times table off by heart. Then, one of the children can take over your role of holding the stick and asking the questions.

Teaching tip

Hold a parent workshop demonstrating how to use a counting stick and sticky notes for times tables so that they can replicate this at home.

Taking it further

To use this idea for division, go through the corresponding division questions as you move along the sticky notes.

Yes game

'I often find my class playing the Yes game in the playground during break times. It is clearly a hit!'

There are some games which can be played for five or ten minutes each day to reinforce mental arithmetic or times tables. This idea is a quick and fun game where the whole class takes part.

Teaching tip

Pick a times table that you have worked on recently to assess their retention and ability to recall it.

Taking it further

You could record an example of the Yes game for your school website and direct parents to it as something they can try at home.

The Yes game is a whole-class game where the children stand in a circle and take it in turns to count in ones. You decide the times table to focus on, for example, the seven times table, and then when a multiple of that number comes up, the child should shout, 'Yes!'

For example: 1, 2, 3, 4, 5, 6, yes, 8, 9, 10, 11, 12, 13, yes, 15, 16, 17, etc.

If a child makes a mistake by saying the number instead of 'yes' or by saying 'yes' at the wrong time, they need to sit down and they are out. To ensure they are still engaged, the children who are no longer playing should keep an ear out and call out anyone who makes a mistake.

The winners are the two children left standing at the end.

You can turn the game into a reasoning activity by giving the pupils a question like 'Year 3 are playing the Yes game. They are working on the 5 times table. If they start on 1, what number is the fifth "yes" going to be?'

Multiple matching

'Referring back to multiples before division lessons meant that the children were noticing patterns without me having to point them out!'

Mixing up multiples and factors is a common issue, but it's important to get right. Explicitly discussing why a number is a multiple of another number ensures the children are secure in the language and secure in the concept.

When you are gearing up to teach division and your class can't remember multiples of six, it feels like you are taking steps backwards. Sometimes, this is ignored, and division is taught regardless of their lack of multiple knowledge. On other occasions, the concept is done to death and the class lose all care for what they are learning. Using a starter like Multiple matching means that the children are revisiting their multiples regularly and using the language of factor and multiple confidently.

Laying out Multiple matching is simple. The factors are lined up down the left-hand side of the page, and the multiples are laid out on the right-hand side of the page. Depending on the year group, you might have one factor, or you might have five. The teacher asks the class, 'Find a multiple of...' and the children must spot multiples of that number.

When taking in answers, the teacher must ask the children to justify how they know they are right. This is where strategies like skip counting, partitioning and related facts can be reinforced and highlighted where appropriate. For example, if a child says, 'I know that 56 is a multiple of four', you could prove this through partitioning 56 into 40 and 16 (two multiples of four) or by saying, 'We know that 12 x 4 is 48, so what happens if we count on in fours?'.

Teaching tip

Have some non-examples on the multiples side of the board to throw potential misconceptions into the mix.

Taking it further

If you want to extend higher-attaining children, ask them to find the largest multiple of the number and explain how they know.

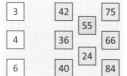

Picturing partitioning

'I had struggled to teach my classes how to partition to help their multiplication until I used the number frames to show it visually.'

Teachers often encourage their pupils to use partitioning as a strategy to help with their mental calculation. This idea demonstrates how to uncover the underlying structure of the mathematics happening when partitioning.

Start with a simple multiplication equation such as 13 x 4. The children will need different-coloured number frames. Ask them to make 13, then ask them to make four lots of 13.

We can partition the 13s into 10 and 3. Then put all the 10s and all the 3s together.

Now we clearly have four 10s and four 3s, which makes calculating far easier. The same can be done with base ten blocks so that they could do this with three-digit numbers too.

When the children have spent enough time using manipulatives to partition and multiply (and this will vary from cohort to cohort and child to child), it is key to move them on to visualising this process. Give them another simple two-digit by one-digit multiplication, such as 18 x 6, and ask them to picture the partitioning step-by-step. Encourage them to make jottings of what they are doing in their heads so they can refer back to it and explain it to you or a partner later on.

If I know... then I know...

'Using related facts to calculate mentally is an important skill in primary mathematics.'

Part of mastery is the ability to manipulate or adjust things to make calculating easier or more efficient. Using this activity when teaching related facts will encourage your pupils to do this independently. This shows true fluency.

Often, the facts that children remember most are the ones using nice round numbers such as 10 or 20. We can use these facts to help with other calculations and avoid using lengthy written methods unnecessarily.

There are two ways of approaching this idea, depending on the competence of your pupils. You could give them the sentence with numbers already filled in or you can give it to them partially filled in to make them do more of the thinking.

Here are some examples:

- If I know 20 x 7, then I know 19 x 7.
- If I know 20 times a number, then I know 19 times a number.
- If I know 20 x 7, then I know...
- If I know 20 times a number, then I know...

All of these lend themselves to children proving the statements using concrete manipulatives or by drawing them out.

Taking it further

Set one of these each week for homework or early work to keep reminding the children of how to use related facts.

Bonus idea ★

Give the class a sheet with four boxes and the statement in the middle. They use the four boxes to do the following four things: show the statement using manipulatives, draw it out, explain it and prove it.

An array of buildings

'I loved this lesson! We got to be creative and learn about multiplication at the same time.'

This is a fun lesson that incorporates multiplication and real-life contexts to engage the children and get them thinking about how we can apply maths in the real world.

Teaching tip

Set the children a homework challenge to use this method to calculate the number of windows on the buildings they see on their way home from school.

Beginning a lesson with a problem or a real-world context that the children can relate to is an effective tool, when used sparingly and accurately. Begin by naming a building the children are familiar with, e.g. the Shard or Beetham Tower, and the question 'How many windows are there?'

Explain to the class that counting the windows in ones, or even twos and fives, would be an arduous task with a huge scope for error. So, we need to find a way around this! But first, explain that they will be creating their own buildings. Give them a range of coloured paper and small yellow squares. They should create buildings based on the following rules: the building must be a rectangle and there needs to be the same number of windows in each row or column. Once they have created their buildings, ask the children to stick them side-by-side on a long sheet of black paper like this.

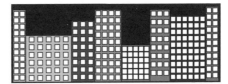

Once this is done, draw their attention to each building. How can we calculate the number of windows? What does the arrangement of the windows remind us of? The children should see that the windows are laid out like arrays, so then you can have a conversation about how to calculate the number of windows on each building.

To move this on, show them a bigger building on the board with a greater number of windows and discuss how to split the windows into more manageable chunks. This could be in rows of ten or five, whatever the children feel most comfortable calculating with.

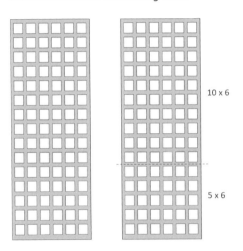

10 x 6

5 x 6

Finally, show the children the original image of the familiar building and discuss how they would go about counting the number of windows.

Target number

'I like to challenge myself by using all four operations to find the target number.'

This idea will benefit the class by developing their ability to see how a number is made up and how to get to a number.

This idea is one that can be developed for any age group by increasing the number and adding more rules.

Give the children a target number, such as 36. Ask them to use multiplication and division (and addition and subtraction if you want) to make the target number of 36. The class can work independently or in groups to find as many different ways as possible to arrive at their target.

There are many different variations of this game, which can make it more or less challenging. For example, you could give the children a time limit of 30 seconds or one minute. To make it more difficult, you might want to give them a selection of numbers to choose from. For older or higher-attaining children, restricting them to a certain number of steps per calculation or by only using three operations will make it more interesting.

Remainder patterns

'Drawing the children's attention to the structure of division meant that they could predict and understand quotients with remainders.'

There needs to be a focus on remainders and why they occur. This shouldn't be a concept that our children find difficult because having 'leftovers' is a completely normal part of everyday life.

There are many ways in which you could approach this style of activity. Regardless of the content, the actual process remains the same.

Take this problem: 'Farmer Jill is boxing up hens' eggs. She packs them into boxes of four eggs. If she has 12 eggs, how many boxes will be full?' That is a standard word problem that most children who have a decent grasp of division will be able to work out easily. But what about when there are 13 eggs? Or 14? Or 15? Can the children predict what might happen if there are 20 eggs? It is this level of discussion and unpicking the structure that will lead to a deep understanding of remainders and why they occur.

Taking it further

When discussing the division behind the problem, encourage and model the use of proper mathematical language (dividend, divisor, quotient) to ensure that verbal and written explanations are clear and that children understand the different parts of division.

Number of eggs	Number in each box	Number of full boxes	Number of leftover eggs
12	4	3	0
13	4	3	1
14	4	3	2
15	4	3	3

This table shows how to approach answering the above in a systematic and meaningful way.

The class could use a manipulative such as counters to help them to fill out the table. This is a real low-threshold, high-ceiling task. Once they have begun to spot a pattern, look at why this is happening. *Why* do we never have 4 leftover eggs?

Grid block

'This had never crossed my mind until I was shown how to scaffold the grid method with concrete manipulatives. Now, it makes total sense to do this with my class before we move on to the more abstract grid.'

Moving on to written methods of multiplication can be challenging for the children to grasp; the grid method is a good mid-point before moving on to the formal method. Laying it out with base ten blocks shows the children what happens when you multiply.

Teaching tip

If you do not have enough base 10 blocks in your classroom but do have access to computers, I suggest using mathsbot. com for your pupils to manipulate the base 10 blocks on there!

As with any method of multiplication or division, the children must have a good grasp of what multiplication is and of their times tables to be successful. Those who are not proficient would benefit from a multiplication grid to give them access to the task at hand.

When multiplying two-digit numbers, it can become confusing for pupils to remember what goes where and why. Using the grid method is a tried and tested strategy for laying the groundwork before moving on to long multiplication.

Take 22 x 13. Model laying out base ten blocks like this:

Then, begin working through the different sections. It is important to start with the ones column as this will mirror our end goal: the formal written method.

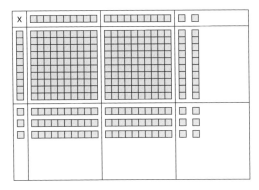

Taking it further

To develop this idea and strengthen the children's understanding, swap the question around by giving them the product laid out in base ten so they have to find the multiplicand and the multiplier.

Using the base ten blocks allows the children to see the physical result of multiplying and gives them a better conceptual understanding, which will help them to move towards a formal written method. While modelling with the base ten, also model the written grid method so that the class are exposed to both.

I do, we do, you do

'This is the structure of my input every single time I am introducing a new method or concept to my class.'

This idea shows you how to structure the teaching of a particular maths topic, particularly written methods or processes with multiple steps, using long division as an example.

Written methods can be tricky to teach, especially when there are lots of steps to go through and a specific order to do them in. Long division is one of those methods that looks intimidating but has a core structure that the children need to remember. So, when teaching long division, or any method, you can use the 'I do, we do, you do' structure.

I do: you model to the class how to do the method without talking and fluently at your usual speed. Then, model again more slowly and stop to point out key moments.

We do: once you have modelled the process to them, first without and then with an explanation, begin to walk them through another example step-by-step. For example:

First, we will list the multiples of our divisor.

Then, teach the method of 1) divide 2) multiply 3) subtract 4) bring down the next number.

$$4\ 5\ 3\ 6 \div 1\ 8$$

```
              2  5  2
    1  8 | 4  5  3  6
           3  6 |
           9  3
           9  0 |
                 3  6
                 3  6
                    0
```

```
        1  8
        3  6
        5  4
        7  2
        9  0
   1    0  8
```

You do: finally, your pupils should have a go on their own.

This is where you and any other adults in the room can circulate and give instant feedback, pick up on any misconceptions and move some children on.

Using the structure of 'I do, we do, you do' when teaching maths means that you give time to explicitly teach them something, then begin to hand some of the responsibility back to them, create worked examples for them to refer to and guide them to working independently. It is far more effective than only doing the 'I do' or the 'we do' parts. Staying silent during the 'I do' section is key because your children need to see a fluent model of how the process works. They need to be able to watch and focus rather than have to listen and watch simultaneously. There is power in your silence!

Taking it further

During the 'we do' section, you can create worked examples for the children to refer back to during their independent practice. This is a powerful and underused teaching strategy but is far more successful than success criteria in maths are.

Grouping or sharing?

'Making the difference between these concepts clear is important for teaching division in KS1.'

This idea looks at two ways of dividing quantities and how to introduce them separately. Often, these two ideas are confused and taught at the same time rather than one at a time.

First, we are going to introduce grouping. This is where we have a quantity of objects that should be put into equal groups of a certain number.

For example: 'Here are 18 socks. How many equal groups of two socks can we make?'

The children could use actual socks or cubes/counters to represent the socks. They need to physically make groups of two until there are no socks left. Next, they can count the number of groups. Then, they can move on to a pictorial representation of the socks, or another object, and circle the equal groups.

Teaching grouping will be at least one lesson and should involve varied questions as well as reasoning-style questions where their understanding is applied to problems.

Next, we can look at sharing. This is when we have a quantity of objects that needs to be shared between a certain number.

For example: 'Here are 12 sweets. Share the sweets equally between six friends.'

Now, the children should practise physically sharing the sweets between the six friends. They should do this one at a time to ensure the sharing is equal.

Again, there should be a varied selection of questions to practise sharing and reasoning problems to assess their understanding.

Fractions, decimals and percentages

Part 4

What it is and what it isn't!

'Some of them were really confusing because they looked like they were going to be halves. The tricks made us learn better, I think!'

The use of standard examples, non-standard examples and non-examples is a vital tool when teaching mathematics.

This activity is best done when introducing fractions, particularly halves and quarters in Key Stage 1, but can be revisited in Key Stage 2 when reviewing prior learning.

First, recap what a fraction is, including parts and wholes, and ensure that the children understand the need for equal parts.

Next, ask them what they know about the fraction 'one half'. Where have they heard it? What does it mean? What does it look like? If the whole is split into halves, how many parts are there in total? Tell them, 'When we are looking at halves, there are two equal parts' and ask them to repeat it or say it to their partners.

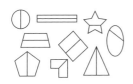

Then, show the children a selection of images and ask them to identify which are split into halves. These should be a range of standard examples that they would regularly see, examples of halves that are not familiar to them and non-examples, which are *not* correct.

Once they have identified the shapes that have been split in half, go through each one and take verbal explanations in full sentences from different children to reach a consensus about each shape. Make sure you focus on why they are and why they are not halves. This will result in a clear definition of halves, which will be invaluable when moving on to quarters and other fractions.

> **Bonus idea** ★
>
> When looking at equal parts, do a similar exercise with shapes that have or have not been split into equal parts and ask the children to explain why each time.

Part–whole relationship spotting

'Before even beginning to look into what a fraction is, children must have a secure grasp of the part–whole relationship in different contexts.'

The relationship between the parts and the whole in fractions is one of the most important concepts for pupils to understand in primary mathematics. Spending a lesson exploring parts and wholes before delving into the meatier fraction objectives is key.

The stem sentence 'If _____ is the whole, then _____ is part of the whole' is key for this idea. Using stem sentences can unlock the barriers some children face with their verbal and written explanations. Put it on your working wall, put it on every slide you use and ask the children to write it in their books. The more used to speaking in full sentences they become, the better.

Start with 'If my body is the whole, then my _____ is part of the whole'. You will need to model this, e.g. 'If my body is the whole, then my head is part of the whole'. Encourage your pupils to come up with their own examples, ensuring they use the stem sentence.

Now show the children a map of Europe with the countries labelled. Model using the stem sentence 'If Europe is the whole, then _____ is part of the whole' and again get them to come up with their own versions. The children can take this as far as they want to. You could then zoom into a map of the UK or a map of wherever your school is located and ask them to do this again.

Next, move on to a collection of objects or things such as a picture of a litter of kittens or puppies, or a group of different-coloured buttons or balls. Again, keep using the stem sentence 'If _____ is the whole, then _____ is part of the whole.'

Teaching tip

To ensure that your class are not becoming overly reliant on it and are truly remembering it, take parts of the stem sentence away as you progress, e.g. 'If _____ is the _____, then _____ is _____ of the _____.'

Taking it further

To really push the most able in your class, give them a journey or distance as the whole, e.g. 'The journey between our classroom and the school office is the whole, so what is a part of the whole?'

Ordering unit fractions

'This made unit fractions so clear for me! Now I will remember that the bigger the denominator, the smaller the parts.'

This is a practical way of showing what unit fractions are, and how to compare and order them. The children will physically make the unit fractions to help their understanding.

Taking it further

You could push this activity forwards by inviting the children to create a fraction wall using these strips of paper.

This activity is best done once children understand the meaning of the numerator and denominator.

To begin with, cut equal strips of paper for the children. The class will need at least five each.

Ask the class to take one strip and fold it into two parts. Explain that the parts must be equal. When they have done this, they should shade one of the parts. Explain that each part is $\frac{1}{2}$ and model labelling the shaded part.

Next, move on to quarters. Tell the class to fold the next strip into four equal parts. Now ask the children to shade one out of four parts and explain that the shaded part is $\frac{1}{4}$.

Do the same thing with eighths.

Remind them that the shaded fractions are unit fractions. Unit fractions are when we are only looking at one part, or when the numerator is one.

Next, ask the class to put the unit fractions in order from smallest to largest. The visual should be clear enough that the fractions go from $\frac{1}{8}$ to $\frac{1}{4}$ to $\frac{1}{2}$.

Show the class the stem sentences 'The greater the denominator, the _____ the parts.' and 'The smaller the denominator, the _____ the parts.' Guide them through filling in the gaps based on what they can see on their strips of paper.

Mixing it up

'The subtle differences between the different representations meant our children were more secure on fractions.'

Shading or identifying fractions of shapes or sets of objects can be a monotonous and routine exercise. This idea offers interesting examples to give your class, which will pay off in the long run as they will have a deeper understanding.

This activity can be applied to any fraction and is a good way of assessing your class's understanding. The task is simple, but the different representations mean the children need to think more deeply about what they are doing.

Start by recapping thirds. What is a third? How do we know when something is in thirds?

Ask the children to shade or circle one third in each of the following examples.

Teaching tip

Use the stem sentence 'One third is one out of three equal parts' to reinforce the concept of the three equal parts. This should mean they avoid the usual misconceptions, e.g. just shading one part regardless of the number of parts.

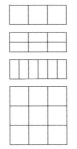
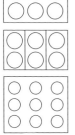

Taking it further

For further practice, the children could have a go at identifying two thirds and explain how this varies what they need to do.

The children will need to think carefully. The process of shading one third of a bar split into three is very different to identifying one third of a set of 12 cupcakes. To do this, the children will need a tight grasp on fractions and how thirds work.

Equivalence bars

'This is the most efficient and simplest way that I have ever seen equivalent fractions taught!'

The concept of equivalent fractions can be a tricky one to teach, especially when the idea of doing 'the same to the top and the bottom' is taught without any conceptual depth or pictorial representations. This idea uses equivalence bars to offer a pictorial representation.

Teaching tip

Model this under a visualiser on squared paper so they can see exactly what you are doing and mimic it.

There are many tricks or chants that children learn in mathematics. One example of these would be 'You do the same to the bottom that you've done to the top', but unless those children have been explicitly shown why this works, they won't have the conceptual understanding necessary.

To start with, model drawing a bar with two equal parts and shade one. Ask the class, 'What fraction is shaded?' and begin to ask how they know. Label the diagram as $\frac{1}{2}$. Underneath draw the same length bar and split it into four parts this time. Shade two of the four parts and ask the class what fraction is shaded and how they know. Label the diagram as $\frac{2}{4}$. Ask the class what they notice about the two bars.

Bonus idea ★

Use the same process of modelling how to draw bars for adding and subtracting fractions with the same denominator but use two different colours to show the different addends.

Then, write $\frac{1}{2} = \frac{2}{4}$ underneath the diagrams. Introduce the concept of equivalent fractions. Explain that equivalent fractions are two or more fractions where the whole is the same but has been split into a different number of parts.

Now, move on to more fractions equivalent to $\frac{1}{2}$ or other pairs of equivalent fractions.

Paper multiplication

'This is the coolest maths hack I have ever seen!'

Operating with fractions can be an incredibly abstract process that is hard for children to visualise or make sense of. This idea is perfect for setting the scene when multiplying fractions.

This activity will show your class the inner workings of multiplying fractions.

Each of the children needs a sheet of plain or coloured paper to fold. Show them a multiplication sentence such as $\frac{1}{4} \times \frac{2}{5}$.

Explain that they need to fold and shade their paper to show the first fraction, $\frac{1}{4}$, by holding the paper in landscape orientation and folding it vertically. They will produce something like the first diagram on the right.

Then, they need to fold and shade the paper horizontally, to show $\frac{2}{5}$.

The overlapped section is the product of $\frac{1}{4} \times \frac{2}{5}$. When we count up the number of parts in total and the number of overlapping parts, we can see that the answer is $\frac{2}{20}$.

Using this method to introduce multiplying fractions is invaluable, as it shows the process of multiplying the denominator and numerator so clearly.

Taking it further

To assess their understanding, give the children pre-folded and shaded paper and ask them to work out which fractions have been multiplied, what the answer is and how they know.

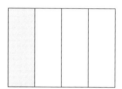

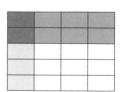

Misconception magic

'Highlighting the misconception first meant they didn't have it later!'

In the addition or subtraction of fractions, the most common misconception is adding or subtracting the denominators. This idea shows you how to tackle the misconception head on.

Instead of hoping they don't turn up, use potential misconceptions as teaching points. For example, here, we know that there will be children who want to add or subtract the denominators so we need to explicitly teach them not to, and why.

Start with a problem such as 'Jenny and Mark are sharing one pizza. Jenny eats $\frac{2}{4}$ and Mark eats $\frac{1}{4}$. How much of the pizza do they eat?'

Show them a solution from a character you come up with, such as a 'Calculation Cat' who always makes mistakes in maths. So, Calculation Cat says 'Jenny and Mark ate $\frac{3}{8}$ of the pizza.' Tell the class that Calculation Cat is wrong and show them why.

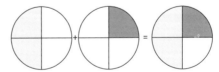

Ask the class what fraction of the pizza Jenny and Mark ate, based on the image above. So what generalisation can they make about adding fractions with the same denominator?

When writing down addition and subtraction calculations when operating with the same denominator, show them like this:

$$\frac{2}{4} + \frac{1}{4} = \boxed{\frac{2+1}{4}} = \frac{3}{4}$$

Decimal wall

'Using a model that the children were already familiar with was such a help when looking at decimal equivalents!'

This idea looks at how we can use a fraction wall to teach decimal and fraction equivalents. A fraction wall is an image that most children in primary school will be used to seeing.

Before introducing the decimal wall, it's important that your pupils are familiar with a fraction wall.

To start with, show them the fraction wall on its own. Ask them questions to get them feeling comfortable and confident using it, such as, 'How many $\frac{1}{2}$ s are in 1?'

$\frac{1}{1}$					1		
$\frac{1}{2}$		$\frac{1}{2}$		0.5		0.5	
$\frac{1}{4}$	$\frac{1}{4}$	$\frac{1}{4}$	$\frac{1}{4}$	0.25	0.25	0.25	0.25

Then, show them the decimal wall alongside the fraction wall. It is important that these images have the same dimensions and colours to emphasise the similarity of the two walls.

Ask the children the following questions:

- What do you notice?
- What is the same?
- What is different?

Push them to notice that 0.5 is the same as $\frac{1}{2}$ and that 0.25 is the same as $\frac{1}{4}$. Ask them what would happen if $\frac{1}{4}$ was replaced with 0.25. Does that change things? Why or why not?

You can start to ask the children questions purely about the decimal wall, such as, 'What happens if you add two lots of 0.25?' This will help them to see the relationship between those key decimal and fraction equivalents.

> **Bonus idea** ★
>
> Create a percentage wall using the same idea, to show the class these key fraction–decimal–percentage equivalents.

Fraction division

'I was tired of rhymes and acronyms for dividing fractions. This idea meant I could show my class what dividing fractions actually looks like in relation to what they already know about dividing.'

Being able to relate dividing fractions to dividing whole numbers is an important link. This idea doesn't offer a quick fix, but it shows the underlying structures of dividing fractions.

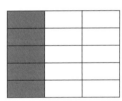

Taking it further

Model the procedure of multiplying by the reciprocal to show your pupils the difference between the two methods. Discuss the advantages and disadvantages of each method.

When we read a division sentence like $45 \div 5$, we say, 'How many 5s are in 45?' So when we have a question such as $\frac{1}{3} \div \frac{1}{5}$, we need to ask: 'How many one fifths are in one third?'

To make it easier, we make our denominators the same. The class should be used to doing this and should see that the lowest common denominator of 3 and 5 is 15. So, we multiply the numerator and denominator of $\frac{1}{3}$ by 5 to get $\frac{5}{15}$ and those of $\frac{1}{5}$ by 3 to get $\frac{3}{15}$.

Now we have $\frac{5}{15} \div \frac{3}{15}$ or 'How many $\frac{3}{15}$ are in $\frac{5}{15}$?'. Show them $\frac{5}{15}$ on a 3 x 5 grid with 5 squares shaded.

Now let's see how many lots of $\frac{3}{15}$ we can fit into our $\frac{5}{15}$, by overlaying lots of $\frac{3}{15}$ on the $\frac{5}{15}$. So $\frac{5}{15} \div \frac{3}{15} = 1\frac{2}{3}$.

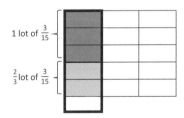

1 lot of $\frac{3}{15}$

$\frac{2}{3}$ lot of $\frac{3}{15}$

Etymology of per cent

'Spending time looking at what per cent means and how it relates to fractions and decimals really secured the concept for my class.'

This idea outlines a specific focus on the meaning of percentages and how this relates to fractions and decimals, rather than jumping straight to calculating percentages.

Etymology is an important aspect of language and vocabulary teaching. Exposing children to the root and background of what they are learning is a valuable way to ensure they understand and remember it. Percent, or per cent, literally translates as 'for every hundred', which cements the idea that percentages are a special type of fraction out of 100.

Ask the children where they have seen percentages before. They might suggest examples such as sales in shops, phone batteries or school attendance figures.

When doing any fraction, decimal or percentage teaching, it is key that the children see that these are different ways of showing the proportion of a number or amount being looked at.

Show them images like the ones below and invite them to estimate the shaded proportion as a percentage.

Then, to reinforce the idea of percentages being 'out of 100', show them shaded hundred squares. Ask the children to label each one with the percentage shaded.

Bonus idea

Give the children a percentage, for example 35%, and ask them to make it using number frames and a 100 base board. They can show it in one block or in parts, as long as they understand that 35% is 35 out of 100.

Pre-sale bars

'This style of question has always flummoxed me as a teacher. I am so glad I have seen this method.'

Calculating the price before a sale deduction, or a reverse percentage, is always a challenge. This idea shows how to represent these problems on a bar model so that the pupils can see the structure of the calculation.

Take the question: 'A laptop is on sale at 35% off. The sale price is £390. What was the original price?'

The inner workings and structure of this style of problem are always a challenge. Generally, children find it difficult to work backwards in this way and errors are made.

A bar model is an excellent tool to show the composition of the problem.

First, we need to draw what the laptop sold for. We know the laptop sold for £390.

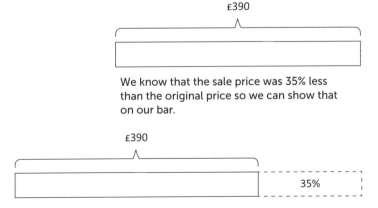

We know that the sale price was 35% less than the original price so we can show that on our bar.

Because we know that 35% was taken off, we can see that the sale price was 65% of the original price, because 100 − 35 = 65.

£390

Now we can use the 65% to help us work out what 100% would have been. We can split the 65% into 5% blocks.

£390

We have 13 lots of 5%. £390 ÷ 13 = £30, so that means 5% = £30. To find 100%, we need to multiply 5% by 20. £30 x 20 = £600 so the original price of the laptop was £600. Alternatively, we could see that 35% = 7 x 5% and multiply 7 x £30 to find £210 and add to the £390 to get £600. It is important that your class understand both ways.

Taking it further

Show the class an already drawn pre-sale price bar model and ask them to create a question to go alongside this bar model.

Dienes decimals

'I didn't even realise you could change the value of the blocks'.

This idea looks at changing the value of base ten blocks (dienes) and using them proportionally so they represent decimal values, so the class can see how the values relate to each other.

Usually the base ten cube is one, the stick is ten and the flat is one hundred. However, we can change the values as long as we are still using them with a base ten proportion.

Use a place value chart to show the relationship between the cubes and the abstract numbers.

ones		tenths	hundredths
1	●		
0	●	1	
0	●	0	1

Show how the decimals and fractions relate.

Base 10	Decimal	Fraction
	1	$\frac{1}{1}$
	0.1	$\frac{1}{10}$
□	0.01	$\frac{1}{100}$

Then ask some comparing and ordering questions, e.g. 0.01 ? $\frac{1}{10}$.

Bonus idea ★

After seeing the relationship between the base ten blocks and decimal to fraction conversion, give the children the flat block that represents one and ask them if they can find the decimal conversion for fractions such as $\frac{1}{4}, \frac{1}{5}, \frac{1}{6}, \frac{1}{7}, \frac{1}{8}$, etc.

Ratio and proportion

Part 5

For every ... there are ...

'Beginning with the stem sentence meant that the children had the opportunity to use language relevant to ratio before being taught what ratio actually is!'

This idea looks at how we can use the language of a concept or a mathematical idea to help introduce what it is. Here we look at the language needed to understand how ratio works.

Start by showing the class an image such as the one below. Give them the sentence frame 'For every two circles, there are _____ squares' and ask them to fill in the blank.

Explain that you will be comparing different quantities using the stem sentence 'For every ... there are ...' Ask the pupils whether 'For every two circles, there are four squares' is the only way to describe the relationship of the shapes in the picture. What about if we said 'For every one circle, there are _____ squares'? How does this change things? What do they notice about the two sentences with the two sets of numbers?

You could move on to fruit or other familiar objects next. Ask the class to show you 'For every three apples, there are nine bananas'. Observe how the children lay out the fruit. Some will place the three apples down first and then the nine bananas, while others will place them using the same method as the circles and squares picture.

Finally, give out a handful of different-coloured counters to each pair in the class. Ask them to write their own 'For every ... there are ...' sentences based on these counters.

Bonus idea ★

Use number rods to demonstrate the 'For every ... there are ...' relationship. For example, place the white 1 rod with the red 2 rod, the red 2 rod with the green 3 rod, and so on. Ask the children to write sentences describing the relationship between the rods.

Posing a problem

'Starting with a problem meant that we had a real context to ratio. This gave our children a better understanding.'

When dealing with topics like ratio, it is important that the children understand how this relates to real life. Giving mathematics a background ensures the children can connect to it.

When you are teaching a new concept, you don't always have to do the explicit teaching or direct instruction part first. In some cases, you might want to introduce a problem to give your new concept a familiar context, and then break it down into the mathematical steps.

For example, 'Cindy, Kate and Bim are baking cupcakes for their class and teachers. A recipe for 12 cupcakes calls for three cups of flour and two cups of sugar. How much flour and sugar do they need for 48 cupcakes?'

Scaling up recipes is a great way of approaching ratio as it is something that the children can relate to real life.

Now they have seen the problem, explain that we see the ratio (one thing compared to another) of flour to sugar as 3 : 2.

We know that 3 : 2 is the ratio of flour to sugar for 12 cupcakes, what about for 48? The children should see the relationship between 12 and 48 and know that 48 is four times 12. So, we need to multiply our flour and sugar ratio by four too.

$3 \times 4 : 2 \times 4 = 12 : 8$

Teaching tip

It would be a good idea to give this to children as a worked example to stick in their books so they have it to refer to when completing their independent work later on.

Taking it further

As homework, you could give the children a recipe for four or six and ask them to scale it up as if they were making enough for the whole class.

How do you like your squash?

'This was so much fun! Not only did I get to drink squash, I perfected my squash ratio!'

Putting maths into a real-life context is an excellent way of making it meaningful for your pupils. This idea engages the children by inviting them to mix up different ratios of squash and taste test them until it's perfect.

Taking it further

Give the class the challenge of finding the perfect squash ratio for everyone at home!

Spend five minutes recapping what ratio is and how to work it out. Ratio should be at the forefront of their minds while they are making their drinks later on.

Explain that today the children will be making orange squash. Demonstrate making a glass of squash by pouring water into a glass and adding the cordial/squash. While you are doing this, explain that there is no science to the way you make your squash and that sometimes it comes out stronger than others. This is why you will be using ratio today to make squash.

To make it nice and simple, make each 'part' a 25ml measure of each liquid. So for a ratio of one part of squash to one part of water (1:1), you will mix 25ml of squash with 25ml of water.

Ask the children to record their findings in a way that works for them; this could be a table or just jottings. The important thing is that they are noting down the ratio of squash to water each time they try something different. You could give them different ratios to try out such as 1:3, 2:5 or 2:3, or you could give them the freedom to try different ratios... there might be some very strange combinations!

Bonus idea ★

Set a similar challenge but with different-coloured paints, e.g. blue and yellow, to find out what ratio of paints mixes to make what shade.

The goal is for them to find their perfect ratio! Each child's will be personal to them, so spend some time at the end sharing who liked which ratio best and why.

Ratio bars

'Using the bar model really helped my class to see how many parts there were in this problem.'

Using a bar model to unveil the structure of a ratio problem is an excellent way to scaffold the process for the children. This idea looks at ratio problems and what the bar models could look like.

Bar models are fantastic for representing the structure of problems in maths. They will not show the answer, so the children need other strategies for calculating, but they demonstrate to the class what a problem looks like.

Take this problem: 'Henry and Demi share football cards with a ratio of 3:4. There are 56 stickers in total. How many does Demi have?'

Without a representation, children might struggle to understand what is happening here. This is where the bar model comes in. We can show Henry's three parts and Demi's four parts on a bar.

Model this and explain that each part is equal. We have seven parts and 56 football cards. 56 shared between seven parts is eight. If the children are not confident with multiplication and division facts, they can physically share 56 between the seven parts to find eight.

If the question asks, 'How many more football cards does Demi have than Henry?' then you could show the bars as a comparative model.

IDEA 54

Fractions to ratio

'The link between fractions and ratio is key to unlocking the children's understanding. I wish I'd spent more time on this when I was in Year 6!'

This idea explores the relationship between ratio and fractions and how to use both ratio and fractions to represent the proportion of a set of objects or amounts.

Taking it further

Move the children on by giving them a problem such as the marbles one. Ask them, 'If there are 25 marbles in the bag, how many of each colour are there?'

To begin with, show the class four cubes or counters (or an image of these) in two colours, e.g. one grey cube and three black.

Ask the class to fill in the blanks of this sentence: 'For every ... there are ...'

We know that for every one grey cube there are three black cubes, so the ratio is 1:3.

Move on to asking the class what fraction of the cubes are grey.

Then ask what fraction of the cubes are black.

The children will know that $\frac{1}{4}$ are grey and $\frac{3}{4}$ are black.

Ask the children what they notice about the numerators. They should spot that the numerators are the same as the numbers in the ratio of 1:3. Ask the class how many cubes there are in total – they should see that the denominator shows us that there are four cubes in total.

Now start with the fractions first. Explain that in a bag of marbles, $\frac{1}{5}$ of the marbles are green, $\frac{2}{5}$ are blue and $\frac{2}{5}$ are red. What is the ratio of blue to green to red marbles? Ask them how they can use the numerators of the fractions to help.

Playing cards proportion

'Our children were used to playing cards, so using them in our ratio and proportion unit made perfect sense.'

The children take their knowledge of ratio and representing proportions and apply it in a familiar context.

In a normal deck of playing cards, there are 52 different cards (without the jokers!). There are four suits and 13 different numbers/letters represented. Within a deck of cards, the potential to ask ratio proportion questions is almost endless.

To begin with, give the children time to explore the cards – this is especially important if they are not familiar with cards. Ask them what colour cards there are and how many suits there are. Tell them the names of the four suits and play a quick game of 'Show me!' to ensure they can recall this information, e.g. 'Show me a club!'

To begin with, ask them a simple question such as, 'What proportion of cards are black?' They might give you the answer $\frac{1}{2}$ or some might not make that connection and give you $\frac{26}{52}$. This is fine to start with and can be explored as you go along.

Next, ask them what proportion of the cards are hearts. Again, some children will recognise that $\frac{1}{4}$ cards are hearts, while others will see $\frac{13}{52}$. Unpick this by asking them what $\frac{13}{52}$ can be simplified down to.

Ask them other questions, such as:
- What proportion of the cards are aces?
- What proportion of the cards are even numbers?
- What proportion of the cards are letters?

Teaching tip

Before you do this activity, spend ten minutes a day for a couple of weeks on introducing different card games to get them used to the cards.

Scale factor shapes

'I use rectangles to start with when teaching scale factors to keep it nice and simple. Then we can move on to different shapes.'

Using and calculating scale factors is vital to be able to determine whether two or more shapes are similar. This idea looks at how you can sequence the teaching of scale factors and similar shapes.

Teaching tip

Model the process of enlarging a rectangle under a visualiser so that the class can see exactly what you are doing during each step.

This idea will span several lessons and is more of a learning journey broken into small steps rather than an isolated activity.

First, you will be teaching how to use scale factors. Give the children a 1 x 5 rectangle on squared paper and ask them to draw it double the size. The concept of doubling is one they should have mastered so this is a good place to start. Explain that to double the rectangle, the length of each side should be multiplied by 2. This process is called enlarging and we enlarge using scale factors. If we are multiplying the side lengths by 2, then the scale factor is 2. Give the children other rectangles to enlarge using scale factors of 2, 3, 4 and 5.

Next, you should move on to calculating scale factors. Here it is important to break the process down. Show the class two rectangles with the dimensions 2 x 3 and 6 x 9 respectively. Ask the class what scale factor has been used to enlarge the original rectangle. Give them the stem sentences, 'Rectangle B is _____ times as big as rectangle A. Rectangle A has been enlarged by a scale factor of _____ to make rectangle B.' Give the class more examples of shapes that have been enlarged and ask them to calculate the scale factors.

Algebra

Part 6

Function machine detectives

'Some of the function machine questions got really tricky but we could work them out eventually!'

This idea shows how to introduce the idea of function machines and finding rules. The class turn into detectives who have to find the function as the numbers go through!

Before the lesson begins, create a function machine! This could be a box with holes on either side for numbers to go in and out of, or it could be a table with a tablecloth for the children to travel through.

At the start of the lesson, explain that you are going to be using a function machine. A function machine takes numbers and turns them into different numbers after performing at least one operation.

Demonstrate this with two cubes. Show the class the two cubes in your hand, place them into the function machine (or go through the function machine with the cubes) and then show the class that the two cubes have increased to become seven cubes. Ask the class what they think might have happened. Do the same with three cubes and come out with eight. Again, let them discuss what the function might be. Take a few answers from around the room. By now, most children will be guessing that the function or rule is +5. Explain that you are going to check by going through again. This time, go in with 10 cubes and ask the children to predict what you will have when you come out of the function machine.

Introduce the words 'input' and 'output' to the class. The input is the number that goes into the function machine and the output is the number once it has been operated on.

Function machine makers

'Trying to trick my friends with difficult rules was the best bit!'

When the class are confident with finding rules of function machines, move on to them being the rule makers. This idea looks at how to structure an activity where the children are making the rules.

To start with, recap how function machines work. Show the class some input numbers and their corresponding output numbers and ask them to find the rule. Start with a one-step rule and then move on to a two-step rule. Ensure they are confident with this before moving on.

Explain that today, they are making the rules. Not the school rules, the function machine rules! Use the same function machine as you have used before and ask a child to come up to the front to demonstrate their own function. Some children might need support with this so be on standby to give them a starting point. Invite the class to guess the function.

Next, pair the children up and give them five minutes to design a function machine for their partner. They need to show at least three pairs of input and output numbers so that their partner has a good chance of working out the rule.

Teaching tip

You might want to give the children a template to keep the presentation neat and tidy, or they could draw it out themselves.

Express expressions

'The work leading up to this lesson is based on years of experience teaching algebra and suspecting that not much of it was sticking!'

After working on function machines and finding rules, the children need to turn this knowledge into being able to write expressions. This idea breaks down that process.

Taking it further

To move this on, do the same but with a two-step function such as x 2, + 4. Model how the unknown input changes as it goes through those two steps.

Spend a few minutes reviewing function machines. Have some counters in your hand, put them through the function machine and then produce more counters. Ask the class what the function is and how they know.

To start the process of writing expressions, show the children a function machine with the function labelled as + 9. Ask the children: 'If the input is 1, what will the output be?', and how they know this. What process did they go through to get the output? Now ask them what the output will be if the input is 5. Again, ask them how they got the output.

Now show them a cube and explain that the cube is your input, but you don't know the value of the cube. If we put the cube through the same + 9 function machine as earlier on, what will the output be? Then put the cube into the function machine and bring it out with nine counters. Ask the children what we have now (cube + 9).

Explain that it is easier to write things down in shorthand. Model this by using 'c' for cube. If the input is c and we put it through a +9 function machine, then the output is going to be c + 9.

Go through more examples where the input is unknown and ask the class to write the expression for the output each time.

Shape substitution

'For some reason, my class felt much more comfortable starting with shapes and then moving on to letters.'

This idea looks at how to introduce the idea of substitution to children and ways to push their thinking forwards.

When letters represent numbers in equations, children can find them daunting. Using shapes to represent numbers is a great way to ease them into substitution.

Show the class the following expression using shapes and explain that each shape represents a number. Where there are two identical triangles, these are the same number.

Tell the class that the circle = 3 and the triangle = 5. Model how to find the value of the expression with these numbers.

Now show the children the same expression using two different shapes. Give the shapes the same value. Ask the children what is the same and what is different about these two expressions. Why is the value the same?

Ask the children to create their own expression using shapes, where each shape is a one-digit number. Take some expressions in and ask the class to substitute the values to find the answer.

Next, show them the expression a + b + b. Explain that a = 3 and b = 5. They will see that the value of a + b + b is the same as the shape expressions. Ask the class why this is. Give them more examples and circulate the room to assess their understanding.

> **Bonus idea** ★
>
> Give the children two equations, e.g. b = 2a + 5 and a = b − 15. Explain that a = 10. Find b and explain how you worked it out. This will give them an idea of how to structure their response.

Bar model equations

'Bar models are essential for children to be able to visualise problems and the structures within problems.'

Using a familiar model such as a bar is a helpful tool to show how to unpick an equation.

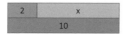

Show children a simple bar model like the one in the margin. Ask them what they notice and what they think this bar represents. Invite them to write out the equation that the bar model is representing, if they can.

Model to the class how the bar model is showing $x + 2 = 10$. Explain that x is an unknown that we need to find. Ask the children to find x in their pairs. Starting with a simple and small case like this is a good way to introduce the concept. If you make it accessible to every child in the room, the underlying structure will make more sense to them all.

Next, show the class another simple equation but this time swap the parts around: it is important for children to see varied examples and understand that the same thing is happening. Ask the class to write the equation that is represented by this bar model. Then, ask them to find x. Again, you are using numbers that the children are familiar with and able to manipulate mentally, which takes the pressure off while they learn a new concept.

Once the class is comfortable with one x, move on to showing them bar models with more than one.

Model how to write these bar models as equations and then model how to find x.

Finally, give the children the equations and ask them to draw them as bar models.

Cups and counters

'Algebra can be such an abstract concept and needs to be introduced both with concrete resources and pictorially before jumping to the numbers.'

Most adults will remember being taught how to solve equations but will not be able to tell you what the process actually is. Using manipulatives will expose the maths behind the algebra and make it less intimidating, as this idea shows.

Using cups and counters to represent your equation is a great way of taking away the fear of algebra and simplifying it down to resources the children know and can use. Take the equation $5x + 3 = 18$.

Taking it further

Show the class an equation where x is not a whole number and ask them to solve it. Look for the point they realise that the cups and counters method would no longer work. What could they do instead? Encourage them to draw their working out.

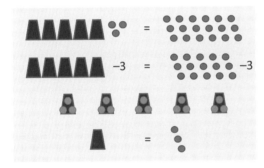

Show your pupils that we always need to keep both sides equal, which is why we take three from both sides at the same time. The beauty of using counters is that we can literally take three away from both sides. Then, we are faced with $5x = 15$. We know that there are going to be no counters left over, so it is a case of splitting what we have equally between the five 'x's. Once we have done that, we can see that $x = 3$.

Model this to the class, as well as the written working out, before giving them their own equation to solve using cups and counters.

Statistics

Part 7

Pictogram problems

'Initially, it seemed that my class had a good understanding of pictograms but I started to ask these questions to push them and it was clear where the gaps in understanding were.'

Once your class has been introduced to pictograms, it is important to assess their understanding with some key questions. These questions can be used to check for misconceptions and deepen the understanding of the most able pupils.

Take this pictogram below. There are lots of different questions that could be asked about this pictogram to assess how deep your pupils' understanding is.

 = 2 goals

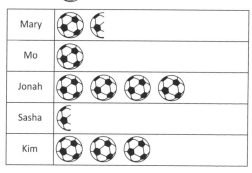

To begin with, ask the children simple and basic questions to see how well they can read the pictogram.

For example:

- How many goals did Jonah score?
- Who scored one goal?
- Who scored the most goals?
- How many more goals did Kim score than Mo?

You might want to ask the class to complete sentences such as: 'There were ____ goals scored in total', 'Mary scored ____ goals' or 'Mo scored ____ fewer goals than Jonah'.

Or you could ask true or false questions by giving them statements such as 'Mary scored two goals'. True or false questions are an excellent tool for asking questions in maths as the children generally feel more secure answering these questions.

Then, you might want to ask questions such as, 'If Sasha is the answer, what could the question be?' to ascertain how well the children are able to interpret the pictogram.

Finally, a classic reasoning question to assess their understanding would be 'Eun-jung says that Kim and Mo scored four goals between them. Do you agree?' and let them give a detailed verbal or written explanation.

> **Bonus idea** ★
>
> Show the class a pictogram with a corresponding tally chart and ask them to work out whether the pictogram has been drawn accurately. Children love correcting other people's work because the onus is taken off them.

IDEA 64

Teaching tables

'I'd never focused on tables for an entire lesson before, but now it seems so obvious that they need to be taught this explicitly.'

Tables are a vital component in teaching statistics. Being able to read them and understand how that data translates onto a graph is an important skill that is often overlooked.

Taking it further

After looking at each table individually, consider their similarities and differences and compare all three at once. Getting the class talking about maths will pique their interest.

Tables are as important to teach as other ways of representing data. A table is a common way to show data but this does not mean that children are innately able to read and interpret them. This is especially important when they start transferring data from a table onto a graph or vice versa.

Below you can see a range of tables that show different data in different ways.

Day	Temp.
Mon	22
Tues	25
Wed	26
Thurs	25
Fri	24

Journey	2017	2020
London to Paris	£54	£39
Paris to Berlin	£37	£29
Berlin to Venice	£65	£42
Venice to Madrid	£55	£34
Madrid to London	£48	£28

	Cheese	Pepperoni	Peppers	Mushrooms
Matthew	X	X		
Hadiza	X			X
Jamal	X	X		
Alice		X	X	X

Spend time on each of these types of table and ask the class questions to assess how well they are able to retrieve information from them.

Questions could be as simple as, 'What toppings did Alice have on her pizza?', 'What was the drop in price between 2017 and 2020 for a ticket from Berlin to Venice?' or 'How hot was it on Wednesday?' to start with. The important thing is that the children are looking in the right places on the tables.

Then, begin to ask questions which are more complex, such as, 'Which children are having cheese and pepperoni on their pizza?' or 'What was the difference in temperature between Friday and Monday?' so that the class have the opportunity to delve deeper into the tables.

A nice way to end this lesson would be to introduce another table and ask the children to generate questions for their peers to answer based on the data in front of them.

Bonus idea ★

When they are secure with tables and you have moved on to graphs, show them a graph that has been drawn incorrectly alongside its corresponding table of data. Ask the class to find, correct and explain the mistakes.

Sort it out

'The subtle changes in each bar chart mean that the children are forced to look at the details and understand how this changes the graph as a whole.'

This idea is a great one to use when introducing or revising bar charts, although it can also be used with other graphs too. It looks at the features of bar charts and how they can change.

This is a nice way to expose your class to a range of bar charts representing different data and using different scales on the axes. You need to find or create at least ten different bar charts. The bar charts should all look different, such as bars of different colours or widths; some charts with vertical bars, some with horizontal; axes using different scales, such as in 1s, 2s, 5s; and so on.

When you have all of your bar charts, print out enough copies for each table or pair. Ask the class to sort the charts into groups. Don't give them any sorting criteria: just see what they come up with. Some will sort by category, e.g. graphs about food or graphs about people, while others will look at the scale and sort that way. Then feed back all together and discuss how each table or pair sorted them.

Finally, go through each bar chart on the board and ask the class these questions: What does it represent? What can you tell me? Which ____ had the most ____? What is the same/different about this graph and the last graph? How many fewer _____ were there on _____?

Before you know it, the class will be reading and interpreting bar charts, without having had to fill out worksheet after worksheet.

To touch or not to touch?

'Making the distinction between discrete and continuous data was really important for my class to be able to construct bar graphs independently.'

This idea looks at the two styles of bar graph and when to use them. Sometimes, we see the bars touching on a bar graph, while on other graphs they are separate. It is important for the class to understand the difference and apply this knowledge when they are constructing graphs.

Discrete data

Discrete data is data that is put into categories and counted, such as the number of pupils or the number of votes an ice cream flavour receives. It can only include certain values: we can't have half a person, for example!

When we have discrete data, the bars do not touch. One example could be a graph in which we look at how many people visited a museum each week over a period of four weeks.

Continuous data

Continuous data is data that is measured across a range of values, such as height or weight. A bar graph using continuous data can take any value within a range, e.g. the number of pupils between 130 and 139.9cm.

When we have continuous data, the bars touch because the scale along the axis is a range of values. One example could be a graph in which we look at the number of trees of a certain height.

Taking it further

Show the class some incorrect examples of graphs and ask them to explain what mistake has been made. Then, they could re-draw the graph correctly.

IDEA 67

The story of a graph

'I love working out what might have happened based on a graph!'

This idea focuses on an activity where children are asked to read a line graph and tell the story with little or no context.

Taking it further

Turn the graph storytelling into homework by sending home a blank graph and asking them to plot an activity they did over the weekend, e.g. taking a bath or going for a cycle.

Graphs tell us a story. We can see what happened over the course of a day, week, month or longer. Being able to read and interpret the line of a graph to work out its story is a skill that all children should have before they leave primary school.

Start by showing them a graph with the axes labelled, such as this temperature graph.

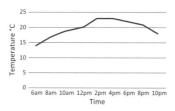

Ask your pupils to discuss in pairs what the graph is telling us. Then, invite one of them to tell the story of the graph based on what they see. At the end, ask the rest of the class if they agree. If anyone wants to challenge the original story, encourage them to tell their own story.

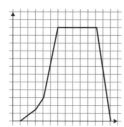

When your class is comfortable telling the stories of graphs like this, move on to graphs that do not have labelled axes, such as the one to the left.

You will get a range of ideas, so encourage the children to be specific about what is happening at each point along the line. Question them along the way to make sure they know exactly why they are telling the story the way they are.

As easy as pie charts

'This was the perfect way to introduce pie charts and then link with fractions and percentages!'

This idea shows how you can introduce pie charts to your class and how you can make the link between pie charts and percentages explicitly clear.

Start by showing the children a pie chart without any values, like the one below. See what information they can get from it. Explain that this is a pie chart. Ask what they think this pie chart is showing. What clues are there?

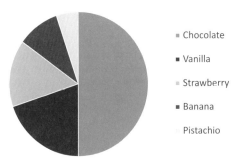

- Chocolate
- Vanilla
- Strawberry
- Banana
- Pistachio

Teaching tip

Where mistakes are made, celebrate them! Show the children that mistakes help to secure and deepen our understanding of a concept.

Taking it further

Move on to a similar pie chart which shows people's choices, with the percentages labelled. Ask the children questions, such as, 'What percentage of people chose _____?' Explain that 200 people were asked. How can they use the percentages to work out how many people chose each category?

Explain that the pie chart shows the favourite ice cream flavours of all the staff at school. If this shows the whole staff, what percentage is the whole pie chart? The children should make the link between the whole and 100%.

If the whole pie chart shows 100%, what can we tell about the different flavours? The children will see that half the staff chose chocolate and will know that $\frac{1}{2}$ is 50%. Based on that, they can start to estimate the rest of the percentages. When someone feeds back their thoughts, make sure you give them time to explain why they think what they think. If they are wrong, question them carefully to make them see where they have gone wrong.

Don't be mean... show them the mean!

'Sometimes formulae and rules need to be shown and laid out to the children so that they can understand why something is the way it is.'

This idea looks at how we can show the mean in a concrete or pictorial way. It focuses on the process of the sum divided by the count.

The mean can be a very abstract concept for children in primary school. The best way of teaching it is to show it visually before throwing a procedure at them. Explain that the mean is a type of average. The children will have probably heard the word average used before.

For example, here we have three children who have eaten cookies and we want to find out the mean of how many were eaten per child.

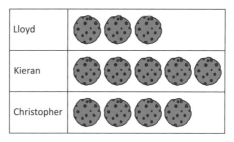

We can see that in total 12 cookies were eaten.

To find the mean, we need to share those cookies between the three children.

Lloyd

Kieran

Christopher

Here, it would be a good idea either to use cookies, or cubes/counters to represent the cookies, and physically show the sharing between the three children.

After this, explain to the children that we have used the sum of all of the cookies and divided them by the number of children. This is how we calculate the mean.

Give the class some similar examples and use the 'I do, we do, you do' approach to model them (see page 44).

After this, move on to numbers. You could use the heights of a group of children in the class. Measure the heights of five children and record these on the board or flipchart. Then, model adding the heights together (to find the sum) and then divide by the number of children measured. The result is the mean of the heights of those five children.

Taking it further

Set the last task as homework. Ask the children to measure the heights of people at home or in their family and find the mean of their heights.

Position and direction

Part 8

Teeny turners

'Now I know about quarter turns and half turns! I loved doing the jump turns!'

Teaching quarter turns and half turns is an important aspect of position and direction teaching in Key Stage 1. This activity is a great way to practise different turns and to get children active.

Taking it further

Show the children images of a person who started facing the front of a room and is now facing the back. Tell them that you think the person has done a quarter turn. Ask them to explain if they agree or disagree with you.

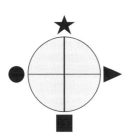

The children should be familiar with the concepts of half and quarter. To review this, show some images of halves and quarters in different contexts to remind the children and get them thinking in halves and quarters.

Print out copies of a circle split into quarters for the children to stand on, with four different shapes placed at each point of the quarters. I suggest printing on A3 paper and laminating them to make them more durable and reusable.

Ask the children to stand in the middle of their circle facing the star and ask them to jump to face the triangle. Explain that this is a quarter turn. Point out the quarters on their mats and make the connection between fractions and turns. Get them to jump back to facing the star. Now ask them to jump to face the square and explain that this is a half turn. Again, point out the fact that they have travelled across half of the circle.

Continue to practise quarter turns, half turns and full turns until the children are able to do them without the fraction mats on the floor.

Then, give them each a toy. This could be a character or a toy car. Instruct them to make their toy do a quarter turn, a half turn and a full turn, until they are confident with this.

Mr or Mrs Robot

'Miss Doherty looked so silly when she was pretending to be a robot! She kept bumping into tables!'

A great way to teach and get the children applying new position and direction vocabulary is to become a robot who can only follow very specific instructions! This idea demonstrates how to use this in the classroom.

A nice way to show the children that you are a robot is to dress up or wear a robot mask. This helps everyone get into the robot mood!

Explain to the class that you are Mr or Mrs Robot and that you want to take a tour of the classroom. You can only move when the children give you directions. Ask a child to direct you to a different part of your classroom.

When the child is directing you, do exactly as they say. They will start off with quite vague instructions such as 'move forward' or 'turn around' so you will need to do what they say. If they don't tell you how far to move, keep moving! Once you have bumped into a few tables (or children!), they will realise that they need to be more specific. This is where you need to remind them of the idea of quarter turns and half turns. Get the children practising the different turns and then ask someone else to direct you to another part of the room. Encourage the children to use other vocabulary too, such as 'left', 'right', 'forwards' and 'backwards'.

Taking it further

Once you have been directed a few times and the children have started using more specific language, pair them up and ask them to direct each other around the room or the school hall.

Robot directions

'I love directing the robots around the grid!'

This idea is closely linked to computing so could be done in either subject. It uses Bee-Bots®, or other similar simple robots, to practise positional and directional language.

To begin with, you will need to teach or recap the key terms, such as forwards, quarter turn, half turn, right, left, clockwise and anti-clockwise. These terms are best learnt with images alongside them to give the children visual representations as well as the terms.

Create cards with different instructions, such as 'three spaces forward' or 'quarter turn right'. Hand out these cards randomly to different pairs or groups and invite the children to place them in any order.

Each pair or group should have enough space to programme their robot so it can move around (around 1m² should do). They should place the robot in the middle of their space and then programme in the different directions on their cards.

Once they have had a go at doing this, they should quickly draw out the route their robot took and label it with the positional and directional language.

Then, ask the groups to move around to have a go at each other's sets of instructions. This would be a good opportunity to see if there are any differences or discrepancies between each group's routes.

Bonus idea ★

Pre-programme the robots and then press 'go' when the children are watching. Ask them to take note of the different directions and turns that the robot is doing.

Coordinate conventions

'This step-by-step process of reading and plotting coordinates meant that our children had a memorable and meaningful way of learning about coordinates.'

This idea looks at how best to introduce coordinates, including reading them and plotting them. It is important that the children don't get mixed up with the x and y coordinates, so this idea looks at some tips and tricks to help with that.

To start with, show your class an image of the first quadrant with a cross mark on a specific point. Explain that you are going to be describing the exact position of that point. Ask the children for ideas of how you could do this.

Go back to the image of the first quadrant with the cross mark. How can we describe the position of this point? 'The point is _____ units along and _____ units up.' Explain that, although accurate, this is a lengthy way of describing the position of a point. Instead of using a full sentence, we use coordinates.

Coordinates are a set of values used to describe the exact position of a point or object on the grid. Coordinates are a pair of numbers. The first number shows us the distance along, while the second number shows the distance up or down. Explain that on the grid, there is an x-axis (horizontal) and a y-axis (vertical). It is important to remember the order of coordinates or the position will not be accurate!

To help the children remember which order the numbers go in, you could put the information shown to the right on posters to put up on the working wall.

> **Taking it further**
>
> Send home a set of coordinates that create a picture or an image when joined by lines. This is a stress-free way of practising plotting coordinates that can be done as homework.

$$(X , Y)$$

$$(\longleftrightarrow , \updownarrow)$$

Translation stem sentence

'Using the stem sentence to support our teaching of translating shapes and coordinates meant that the pupils had a solid base to start with.'

Stem sentences are crucial when teaching mathematical explanations. Often, our pupils do not have a good enough grasp of the English language to form sentences with new vocabulary to describe or explain a concept.

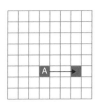

To begin with, show the class an image of a simple one-step translation (see left). Here, shape A has been translated. Ensure that you draw attention to the fact that the shape has not changed in size; it has just been moved.

Give the class the stem sentence 'Shape A has been translated _____ right/left' and ask them to fill in the gaps. Show them more one-step translations (horizontal and vertical) to get them used to using the full stem sentence.

Teaching tip

To ensure the children use the stem sentences regularly and confidently, ask the class to repeat them several times in different groups as well as all together.

When they are comfortable with these one-step translations, show them a two-step translation such as the one on the left.

Give the class the stem sentence 'Shape A has been translated _____ right/left and _____ up/down'.

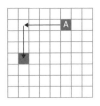

At first, show the translation with the arrows and then slowly take them away so the children become more used to working out the translation independently.

Once the class are confident translating on a blank grid like the ones here, move them on to translating shapes in the first quadrant as a stepping stone before you begin to incorporate coordinates.

Plotting predictions

'The ability to spot the pattern in the coordinates and visualise the shape shows a true fluency and mastery of coordinates.'

This idea is an interesting activity to do once your class has learnt how to plot coordinates on a grid. It will assess how deeply they understand how coordinates work and will develop their visualisation skills.

To begin with, recap plotting coordinates. Depending on the year group, this could be in the first quadrant or in all four quadrants.

When your class are used to plotting coordinates and shapes, it is a good idea to see how well they can visualise what a collection of coordinates will look like once plotted.

For example, if you have the coordinates (1,1), (1,5), (5,5) and (5,1), what shape will it make?

The children could picture the grid in their heads and work out what it would look like, or they could look at the number of points and the difference between the numbers. Encourage them to see that as we have four pairs of coordinates, it therefore must be a quadrilateral. Then, we can look at the fact that we only have 1s and 5s and decipher that the sides of the quadrilateral must be equal. This means the shape is a square.

Here are some other plotting prediction shapes to give them:

- (3,8), (3,-2), (7,8), (7,-2)
- (-1,-4), (3,-4), (1,2)
- (-5,2), (-2,2), (-2,5), (1,5)

Teaching tip

Reveal the shapes one point at a time, so that anyone who hasn't yet guessed what shape it is can begin to guess as the points are revealed.

Routine reflection

'Working one point at a time was key to successful reflections.'

Reflecting shapes should be a simple and straightforward task but mistakes are often made. This idea shows how a step-by-step sequence can result in more accurate reflections.

To demonstrate reflection, show the children a shape that has been reflected in the y-axis.

Ask the class how they know the shape has been reflected in the y-axis. What do they notice about the distance between the y-axis and the points? Ask the class to write down the coordinates of the two shapes. What do they notice about the coordinates? How will that help with checking the accuracy of reflections?

Next, show the class a non-example of reflection. Ask them what they notice. Question them about what is wrong with it and where the reflection has gone wrong.

Now they have seen reflection and are beginning to understand how it works, model how to reflect a shape in the x- or y-axis. The most important thing here is that they are doing it one point at a time.

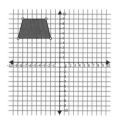

Model numbering or lettering the points to give the class a clear order to work through. Show them how to count the distance between the points and the mirror line/axis and then count the distance on the other side.

Shape

Part 9

Shape sorter

'Even *I* didn't know some of these shapes fit into multiple definitions!'

To learn the properties of different shapes, children need to be familiar with the types of properties there are and what they look like in shapes. Then, they can work out which shape is which based on different definitions.

First, you need to run through the different 2D shapes that you are looking at. This will depend on your year group so only choose shapes that your class need to learn. Simply ask them to name the different shapes and do some rapid recall of the shape names.

Then, go through the different properties of shapes on a general level. For example, sides, corners, angles, parallel sides, equal sides, etc. Again, spend a few minutes quizzing the class on the properties.

Now, give them a pile of definitions of shapes and a pile of shapes and ask them to match these up. They can do this in pairs so they have someone to discuss and bounce around ideas with.

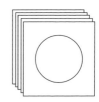

This shape has two pairs of parallel and equal sides and four right angles.

Come back together as a class and share your findings. If there are differing answers, or definitions that could belong to two shapes, discuss these as a class and spend time picking apart the definitions. This kind of thoughtful and rich discussion in mathematics is vital for children's mathematical reasoning capabilities.

Carroll quadrilaterals

'This activity introduced my class to Carroll diagrams and ensured they were thinking deeply about quadrilaterals.'

This idea will help you to dedicate the necessary lesson time (and post-lesson time) to teaching the children about the quadrilaterals they need to know, and discussing them.

A Carroll diagram is a powerful way to sort objects, numbers or shapes based on their traits.

This idea looks at focusing on two aspects of the properties of quadrilaterals: parallel sides and right angles. Give the children a range of images of quadrilaterals, standard and non-standard, and ask them to sort these into the Carroll diagram based on the categories. Doing this in pairs would encourage verbal reasoning.

Teaching tip

Print and laminate blank Carroll diagrams and write the categories on in a whiteboard pen so you can reuse them in a different lesson.

	One or two pairs of parallel sides	No parallel sides
Right angles		
No right angles		

Once they have done this, you can discuss as a class how they sorted the shapes and look for any inconsistencies between groups to work out who is right or wrong, and why. This idea will continually reinforce the concepts of parallel sides and right angles as you will be constantly reminding and questioning them about what these concepts mean.

Bonus idea ★

Spend time sorting the quadrilaterals into a Venn diagram with different categories, in order to reinforce the different properties and ensure they are overlearning the shapes.

Geoboard geometry

'I love using geoboards because I don't need to worry about making mistakes in my book!'

This idea looks at geoboards and how to incorporate them into your shape work. Geoboards are a versatile piece of equipment that can be used across primary maths lessons.

A geoboard is a flat wooden or plastic square with an array of pegs sticking up. They can be used with elastic bands to create shapes and images. Geoboards can usually be found in most primary schools but are often not used to their full potential.

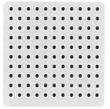

There are a range of activities you can do with a geoboard. For example, you might want to give each child an elastic band and direct them to make a specific type of triangle, or a square, or a different quadrilateral. You might direct them to make an irregular pentagon. The possibilities are endless when it comes to creating shapes. You could ask the children if they can make a circle and then discuss why they couldn't.

You might want to focus on quadrilaterals by asking them to create a quadrilateral with two right angles, or one set of parallel sides. Alternatively, you could ask them to create different rectilinear shapes.

You could delve into the topic of area and ask them to create a shape with an area of four, or you could do the same with perimeter.

3D soapy shapes

'Dipping our structure into the soapy water meant we could lift it out and see the different faces.'

Sometimes you need to do something hands on... preferably with sweets! This activity lends itself so well to starting to learn the properties of 3D shapes.

Every now and then, we are faced with what can be a dry unit of work in maths and it is our job to make it less dry. I have always found that my class are instantly more invested in a lesson when there's food involved – so why not go out and buy some midget gems for a lesson on 3D shapes?

The children need to have a basic understanding of what 3D shapes are before they can access this lesson. I would recommend a lesson on identifying the 2D shapes on the surface of 3D shapes and learning the names of the 3D shapes before moving on to building them.

Your class will need cocktail sticks and midget gems or just balls of sticky tack. They can work in pairs or independently. You will need to select some basic 3D shapes such as a cuboid, pyramid or triangular prism and invite the children to construct these shapes using their cocktail sticks as edges and the sweets as vertices. The children will work at different paces, so I would have plenty of extra available for them to make more.

When they have completed their 3D shape structures, they can take it in turns to dip their shape into a bowl of soapy water. As they pull the shape out of the water a bubble forms, meaning that each face has a film between the edges. This makes a great photo opportunity: the children can annotate the picture later with the faces, edges and vertices.

Taking it further

Include spheres and cylinders in the selection of shapes and ask the children to consider why it was not possible to create these 3D shapes with the materials provided. You might also want to discuss why a cube would be a more difficult shape to construct!

Angles on a table

'I loved being an angle detective!'

Remembering types of angles can be difficult for children. This idea allows you to assess their knowledge of angles and gets them up and about – by drawing on the table!

Writing on the tables is always exciting for the children and will instantly interest them in this activity. Before the lesson, spend time placing easily removable tape, such as masking tape, in different directions on the tables in the classroom.

Ask the children to move around the room and label the different angles made by the tape on the tables. Depending on the year group, this could simply be 'acute', 'obtuse' and 'right', or you could add 'reflex' and 'straight' in there too. They should write the different types of angle on the table using a whiteboard pen (it will wash off!), as well as going around to check the angles labelled by other children to ensure accuracy.

If you are doing this activity in Years 5 and 6, you might want to invite the children to measure the angles with a protractor and write the answers on the table with a whiteboard pen. Again, they can use their protractors to check each other's measurements.

The adults in the room can observe and question the children to assess their understanding of angles and give instant feedback.

After this task, it is vital to then transfer what they have done into specifically chosen and well-designed questions to assess their understanding.

Protractor procedure

'I found the repetitiveness of this activity was the best way for the class to become masters at measuring angles!'

This idea focuses on using the same language and a verbalised routine to practise using a protractor to measure angles.

When using a protractor, it can be easy to make mistakes. Your pupils will need instructions to follow and a routine to go through before measuring angles accurately can become automatic.

The easiest way to teach your class how to measure angles accurately using a protractor is to use this routine and talk through it almost like a script.

First, we estimate the angle. Does it look like it is greater than or less than a right angle?

Next, we place the origin of the protractor on the corner of our angle.

Then, we rotate the protractor so the base line aligns with one leg of the angle.

Now, follow the other leg of the angle up to the measurements on our protractor.

If the base leg of the angle is to the right, we use the inside measurements of the protractor; if it is to the left, we use the outside measurements of the protractor.

Model this process once so the class can see you doing it and then go through the process again with them following along. Then, give them a chance to do an example on their own and assess how they get on.

Encourage the class to go through the steps out loud or in their heads to ensure that they are not rushing or making mistakes.

Teaching tip

Pair the children up and encourage them to talk each other through the process of measuring angles using a protractor, ensuring they follow each step properly before they do it independently.

Etymology of triangles

'I had never thought about using the root of shape names to teach them, but now I know how much it helps!'

This idea looks at how you can use this to teach the different triangles. Using the etymology of words is a great way of introducing new vocabulary.

Teaching tip

Have a look at other mathematical terms which have Latin or Greek etymology that can be used to teach the meaning of the words, e.g. numerator and denominator.

There are four types of triangle: equilateral, isosceles, scalene and right-angled.

Equilateral triangles

This comes from the Latin term aequilaterus. 'Aequus' means even, and 'later-' means side, so aequilaterus means equal-sided. Link the 'equ' at the start of equilateral to the start of equal. This will help your class remember that equilateral triangles have equal sides.

Isosceles triangles

This name comes from the Greek root 'isos' which means equal, and 'skelos' which means legs. So the isosceles triangle has two equal legs (or sides) and a base of a different length. A visual showing the sides of the triangle as legs would be helpful.

Scalene triangles

This comes from the Greek word 'scalenos' which means uneven: we can relate this to the uneven or unequal sides of a scalene triangle. This will help the class to remember that scalene triangles have three unequal sides.

Right-angled triangles

There is no Latin or Greek meaning here as the key thing in a right-angled triangle is the right angle. The children will be familiar with right angles so should be able to spot them in a triangle. Ask your class, 'Can a triangle have two right angles?'

Tearing triangles

'My mind was blown away when I saw this!'

This idea is a great way of proving that the angles in a triangle equal 180°. Sometimes we teach these things without showing them, which can result in insecure understanding.

Before you move on to the angles in a triangle, your class should be secure with right angles and angles on a straight line. You might want to review these before you move on to this activity.

Ask the children to draw a triangle on a piece of card or paper and cut it out. Once they have made their triangle, tell them to tear the corners off so they have the three angles from the triangle.

Tell them to arrange the corners to make a straight line.

Ask the class what they notice. What does this mean? How does this show us what the angles in a triangle total?

Tell the class to measure each angle and add them up. They will find that the angles of the triangle do indeed equal 180°.

Encourage the class to repeat the activity two or three more times to show that this is always the case and that the angles in a triangle always add up to 180°.

Teaching tip

Model this under the visualiser so that the class can see exactly how you are tearing the triangle and arranging the corners.

Taking it further

Send this home as a practical activity for the children to demonstrate to an older sibling or adult at home.

Bonus idea

You can do the same activity with a quadrilateral. Put the four corners together; this will look like angles around a point. We can see that angles around a point and the angles in a quadrilateral equal 360°.

Pixel art

'I loved making the pictures look the same on both sides of the line!'

This idea is a great way of introducing the concept of symmetry. Before pupils can identify symmetry in shapes, they must understand what something looks like when it is symmetrical and practise creating symmetrical images.

This could either be done as a recap-style starter before looking at the symmetry of shapes, or used within a lesson introducing the concept of symmetry.

To start with, show the class an image such as the one below, where there is a line of symmetry marked out and both sides of the image are the same. Ask them, 'What do you notice?' and 'How can we be sure that each side is the same?'

You could count squares or mark off squares that have been shaded on each side, one at a time. Or, you could model how to use a mirror to check that each side is the same. Show them how to place the mirror along the line of symmetry and check that the reflection matches what is on the image.

Set the class the task of creating symmetrical images. If this is new for your class, you could give them a half-finished grid, on which they have to reflect the image along the line of symmetry.

Next, give them blank grids like the ones below where the line of symmetry changes. The vertical and horizontal lines of symmetry are best to start off with, whereas the diagonal line of symmetry is a good challenge for more able pupils. To really challenge them, ask them to create an image with two lines of symmetry.

Bonus idea ★

Show the class a pixel art image without the line of symmetry. Ask them to find the line of symmetry. Is there more than one? How can they be sure?

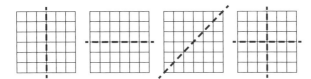

Finally, provide the class with blank grids without any lines of symmetry marked and ask them to create a symmetrical image.

Investigating angles

'Sometimes, a carefully constructed activity where the children appear to be discovering the learning themselves is the best way to cement a concept.'

This idea shows how you can design a task that on the surface looks like a discovery investigation but is really a specifically chosen task that will highlight a certain concept. In this case, it is the idea of opposite angles being equal.

Ask the class to draw an X on their page. Then, tell them to use a protractor to measure the angles. What do they notice? What is the same? What is different?

They will notice that the opposite angles are equal. This is called vertically opposite angles. The 'vertically' aspect relates to the vertex, which is where the lines cross.

Ask them if they think this is a one-off or if it will happen every time. They could write down a prediction in their books or just tell their partner what they think.

> **Bonus idea** ★
>
> Once the children are confident with vertically opposite angles, give them more complicated problems to solve, such as missing angle questions where only one angle measurement has been given and they need to work out the other three.

Next, ask the class to try out some different examples to investigate whether or not opposite angles are always equal. This could lead to an interesting discussion about how many examples is enough to prove a theory.

Although your pupils will feel like they are discovering this on their own, you have crafted an activity to expose a new concept to them. This is an excellent way of approaching a concept like this – one where it can be proved or disproved by creating more examples.

Always, sometimes, never

'These questions give children the opportunity to reason and prove statements, which is something they feel more comfortable doing than having to find the answer to a question.'

The use of 'always, sometimes, never' questions is something I reserve for teaching the properties of shape. While they are regularly used in some schemes of work for number questions, there are no 'sometimes' rules in number. It either is or isn't true. In geometry, however, there are 'sometimes' cases, e.g. a square is always a rectangle but a rectangle isn't always a square.

This can be used after you have taught and practised the different shape properties for your year group. It will assess how well your class has remembered the properties and push them to think more deeply about 2D shapes.

You can give the class anything from one to five statements. They need to go through and work out whether each statement is always, sometimes or never true. They should prove it with a variety of examples using both drawings and a written explanation.

For shape, you could give the following statements:

- A square is a rectangle.
- A pentagon has five corners.
- A rhombus has four right angles.
- Triangles have a line of symmetry.
- Quadrilaterals can be cut into two equal triangles.

The most interesting part of this activity is seeing the children debate and prove their answers.

Bonus idea ★

Provide the children with instructions or boundaries for drawing shapes, such as 'Draw a triangle with a line of symmetry' or 'Draw a pentagon with five unequal sides'.

Measurement

Part 10

Non-standard measuring

'This step is essential to secure the concept of measuring the height of objects around the classroom.'

The process of teaching children how to measure accurately is one that takes careful teaching. This idea looks at how to use objects that our children are familiar with, such as cubes or handspans, to introduce the idea of measurement.

Taking it further

At the start of the next lesson, ask the children to measure something with their feet or hands, while you do the same with yours. Ask the children why you have different measurements to them, and move on to explaining that we have universal units of measure.

With teaching height, length and width, we have a whole host of new vocabulary that many of our pupils will not be familiar with or will not be confident using. An important step early on in teaching measurement is the use of non-standard units of measure.

To start with, choose objects around the classroom such as a reading book, a chair, their carpet area, a bookshelf or a pencil. Then, model how to use other objects to measure how long, tall or wide something is.

Start with a pencil and ask them to see how many cubes long the pencil is. Explain that when we use objects to measure, we need to use objects of equal length. Give the children the sentence structure of 'The pencil is _____ cubes long.' Give them time to measure their own pencils and ask them to measure a whiteboard pen or the edge of their maths book with the cubes. Ask them to write the sentence to describe the length of those objects.

Now move on to handspans. Show them a larger object such as a bookshelf or the interactive whiteboard. Ask them if using cubes would be the best method. Explain that we can use our hands to measure the height or length of an object and model this to them. Then, ask the children to use their handspans to measure the length and width of their tables.

Capacity comparison

'Our class couldn't believe how wrong their predictions had been!'

This idea shows how to use varying sizes of containers to deal with misconceptions about capacity.

Show the class a range of similarly shaped but different-sized containers, such as tubs or bowls. Ask the children to put them in order, from the container that will hold the least to the container that will hold the most.

This should be a fairly simple task as they will be used to comparing the height of objects by now. To prove their accuracy, fill each container with beads or cubes and then count how many fit into each one.

Next, give the children a broader range of container shapes and sizes. Ask them again to put them in order from the container that holds the least to the one that holds the most. This will take longer and should produce some interesting talk!

Once the children are happy with the order, ask them to go through the same process of seeing how many beads or cubes fit into their containers to check how accurate their choice of order is.

Have a class discussion about where some of them made mistakes in their order and discuss why this might have been.

Teaching tip

Have four or five groups using the same range of tubs so that the whole class can take part in a discussion about the specific containers.

Taking it further

Send home the same activity as home learning: ask the children's parents or guardians to help them to choose different containers from around the house and discuss which holds the least or most.

Bonus idea ★

Do the same activity again, but this time fill the different containers with water to provoke a discussion around volume and how we can check which is holding more.

Apples and oranges

'This is an interesting and fun activity that gets younger children talking about mass without any pressure to write things down or answer complicated questions. The depth of understanding can be developed through talking and verbal questioning.'

This activity builds on previous learning on comparing the mass of different objects. It moves on to comparing groups of objects and then balancing different quantities of objects.

Teaching tip

When balancing the scales, try not to choose very light or very heavy objects as you might never manage to balance them!

Taking it further

Ask the children to try estimating how many of one object weighs the same as how many of another at home. They can do this independently or with an adult or sibling.

To start with, recap how to use scales to compare the mass of two different objects, such as an apple and an orange. Give the children the stem sentence 'The _____ weighs _____ than the _____' to use when describing the mass of the two objects. Then, remind the children that the less than and greater than signs can be used here.

Move on to weighing two of the lighter object, for example, here it could be the orange. Give the class the stem sentence, 'Two oranges weigh _____ than one apple' or 'One apple weighs _____ than two oranges'. Continue to experiment with three of one and two of the other, and so on.

Now, introduce the idea of balancing the scales. You can continue using the same objects or you can use other objects, such as cubes and counters or eggs and tennis balls. Explain to the class that they need to work out how many of one object weighs the same as how many of the other and explain their findings using the stem sentence '_____ _____ weighs the same as _____ _____', e.g. 'Three eggs weigh the same as ten tennis balls'.

The rules of the ruler

'Knowing how to use a ruler accurately cannot be taken for granted. I find spending the time on it in Key Stage 1 saves time later on.'

This idea breaks down how to teach measuring accurately with a ruler. It provides almost a script that your pupils can use until it becomes second nature.

Measuring accurately using a standard ruler can be tricky for younger children, especially if their knowledge of zero and what zero means isn't secure. There are many potential misconceptions when measuring, so it is important to give it enough time and attention early on.

Children need to be explicitly shown how to line up the start of what is to be measured with the zero line on the ruler. The best way to do this is under a visualiser so the class can see exactly what you are doing. You might want to measure a range of objects, such as the edge of a book where it is effectively a straight line, or a pencil where lining up the edge is not as simple.

Teaching tip

Where objects are giving decimal lengths, have the children use the nearest whole number.

Each time you model measuring an object, say out loud, 'I start at the zero and measure up to _____. The object is _____ long.' This will reiterate the rule again and again. Then, give them time to measure objects on their tables and walk around to observe who is following the routine of lining up to the zero to accurately measure their object.

Finally, move on to measuring lines. To ensure the lines are easy to measure, make sure their lengths are in whole numbers and get the children to measure in centimetres or millimetres.

Seeing doubles

'Using this when teaching the perimeter of rectangles draws the children's attention to how they can use doubles.'

The ability to make links between different concepts or to use one concept to aid another will help them greatly. This idea will encourage the children in your class to spot doubles when approaching the perimeter of rectangles.

Give your class a 'true or false?' question for homework using the same principle from this idea, such as 'True or false? This calculation shows someone working out the perimeter of a rectangle? 24m x 3 + 12m = 84m'. Ask them to write down a written explanation as to why it is true or false.

First, revise doubles with the class. A simple round of 'ping-pong', where you shout a number and they shout back the double would be a nice way to start this idea. Or play a game of 'Splat!' where the children take it in turns to play against each other and splat the doubles on the board.

Then move on to looking at rectangles. Remind them that the perimeter is the distance around the outside of a 2D shape. Show them some rectangles and ask them what they notice about the sides. They should spot that the opposite sides are equal. Then, you can show them how they can pair up the equal sides and use their doubles knowledge to find the perimeter.

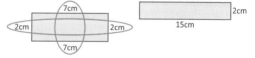

Bonus idea ★

Introduce the formula perimeter = 2(length+width) or P = 2(l+w) or P = 2(a+b). It may seem daunting to introduce a formula to the class but this early introduction to algebra is a perfect way to teach the perimeter of a rectangle.

$(7cm + 2cm) \times 2 = 18cm$

$(15cm + 2cm) \times 2 = 34cm$

Once the class are used to spotting the doubles and using them to calculate the perimeter, they can move on to rectangles with only two sides labelled. They will be able to transfer their knowledge of rectangular perimeter and doubles to add the two labelled sides together and double the total.

Estimating irregular areas

'My class really struggled to see what the area of an irregular shape or a shape with curved edges might be. Breaking it down into these steps meant that they had a process to rely on.'

This idea investigates how to estimate or work out the approximate area of an irregular shape that is not rectilinear.

Show the class an image of an irregular shape on a squared grid like the one below. Explain that this is the proposed pond for the playground and that they need to work out the area so we know how much to dig.

Taking it further

You could turn this into an outdoor learning lesson by drawing out the grid and shape in the playground.

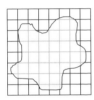

Because this is not a simple rectilinear shape, we need to break things down into steps.

Step 1 is to count the number of whole squares. Encourage the children to mark the squares once they have been counted to avoid double counting.

Step 2 is to look at the parts of squares that we can see.

Step 3 is to consider which of these parts we can put together to make whole squares.

Step 4 is to look at the rest of the parts and see if they will make whole squares.

Emphasise that this is merely an approximation rather than an exact area.

Give the class more questions like this and encourage them to follow each step, noting down their answers each time.

Odd one out

'This activity provides pupils with the opportunity to justify their thoughts using mathematical vocabulary and reasoning.'

This idea asks your pupils to hone in on the specifics of a concept to work out the odd one out. In this case, they will be looking at the area and perimeter of different shapes.

Teaching tip

This works well when you have developed a classroom culture of open discussions with no fear of making mistakes. Make sure any additional adults in the classroom know this is the classroom ethos, especially in maths.

This idea looks at a range of shapes and asks the children to spot the odd one out.

Give your pupils a selection of shapes, for example, you could give them four shapes with the same perimeter but different areas. They will need to draw on the knowledge that they have learnt over the course of your maths lessons on perimeter and area to work out the differences.

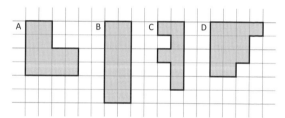

Ask them to decide which the odd one out is. They should talk this through with a peer and listen to other explanations. Then, they should give a written explanation using full sentences and mathematical vocabulary.

Bonus idea ★

Odd one out activities are great to get the children talking. You could give them four numbers or images that have no clear odd one out and get them to talk about which they think it is.

Some pupils might have different answers to each other, or to the one you had been planning, and that is fine if their justification is solid. For example, while you might have said that C is the odd one out because it has an area of 7cm², someone might say that B is the odd one out because it is the only rectangle.

Kicking off conversion

'This prelude to teaching converting units was vital in cementing the mathematical knowledge and skills necessary.'

This idea is a starter or pre-teaching lesson to use before teaching converting different units of measure.

A solid understanding of how place value works is crucial for most areas of primary mathematics, especially converting units of measure. Our pupils need to understand that we have a base-ten system and what that looks like.

To start with, you should give them the number 1 and ask them to multiply it by 10, then 100, then 1,000. Give them a different one-digit number and ask them to multiply it by 10, 100 and 1,000.

Next, look at what happens when you divide by 10, 100 and 1,000. They should be comfortable with decimals but if they need a scaffold then you could use a Gattegno chart to support them (see page 13).

When they do this, make sure that you are using a consistent stem sentence such as, 'When you multiply/divide by ___, the digits move ___ place(s) to the right/left' as this will help with the pupils' verbal explanations and understanding of the process. At no point should you be saying the decimal point moves or that we add or take away zeros, and if the children say it then make sure to correct them using the above stem sentences.

Next, give the children a selection of missing number questions such as those on the right. The class will need to use their knowledge of multiplying and dividing by 10, 100 and 1,000.

When they are secure with this, you can introduce different units of measure and how they can be converted.

Teaching tip

Stick the stem sentences up on your working wall as a constant reminder for the class.

Taking it further

This idea can be developed into a regular five-minute morning activity to continually reinforce the process of multiplying and dividing by 10, 100 and 1,000.

$5 \times$ _____ $= 5,000$
$60 =$ _____ $\times 100$
_____ $= 0.4 \times 1,000$
$10 \times 0.07 =$ _____
$25 \times$ _____ $= 2,500$

Time to break it down

'I used this method to teach time and every single child "got it".'

This idea looks at breaking down how we teach telling the time on an analogue clock. It is best used as a whole-school approach.

Break down telling the time by starting with just the hour hand. Lay sticky notes or cards with the numbers 1–12 on them in a line. Explain that each number is the number of hours, so when the arrow points to 4, it is four hours, which is what we call four o'clock. Point to different numbers and ask the children what o'clock it is. Then, you can move your sticky notes into a circle representing the numbers on a clock with the arrow in the middle. Explain that this arrow is called a hand. You can question the children about the time, e.g. 'What number is the hand pointing to?', 'What time is it?' and 'What time will it be in one hour?'

When the class have mastered the hour hand, you can move on to teaching half past. Go back to the numbers 1–12 laid out horizontally. Show the children the arrow halfway between two numbers and explain that this is halfway past the hour. Again, show the class different half past times and question them. Then, you can move those numbers back into a circle to show the whole clock with the hour hand still in the middle. Keep giving them different examples of half past the hour and push them with questions like, 'What time will it be in half an hour?' You can repeat this to teach quarter past and quarter to.

Teaching the minute hand will be easier now. The minute hand can be broken down in the same style.

Money, money, money!

'The time spent on the different denominations of notes and coins will result in more confident and competent money work later on in primary school.'

This idea is a lesson, or sequence of lessons if your class need it, built up of a mixture of identification and sorting. The overlearning of the different notes and coins, paired with needing to know 'which is more', is vital to ensuring our pupils have firm foundations for using money.

To start with, spend time on each coin and note. Ask the class questions such as: 'What colour is it?', 'What shape is it?', 'What is the value of the coin?' and 'How do you know it's a _____ coin?'

Then, flick through pictures of the different coins and notes and ask the children to rapidly recall which coin or note it is. If you have a teaching assistant, ask them to keep an eye on who is responding accurately, who isn't always responding accurately and who isn't responding at all so you know who to make your focus children for this lesson.

Move on to sorting the coins into piles. They will need a range of fake coins to share with a partner. Shout out instructions such as, 'Sort the coins into piles of copper, silver and other coloured coins!' or 'Sort the coins into less than 20p, equal to 20p and more than 20p!'

When the class have shown their competence with identifying coins, take the pictures away and describe a coin to them. For example, 'I am thinking of a coin. It is a silver coin. It is a circle. What could my coin be?' and they will have to give any and all possible answers.

Teaching tip

When talking about money, make sure that the children are exposed to different ways of describing money, e.g. 'p' and 'pence'.

How many ways?

'This activity was an excellent way to stretch my class's understanding of coins and money.'

Knowing which coins can be used to generate an amount of money is something that many children find difficult. This idea will help them to spend time practising and mastering this.

Taking it further

Introduce restrictions to the problem to make it more challenging, either for the whole class or just the most able pupils. Restrictions could be things such as, 'You can use a maximum of ten 1p coins.'

Once your class are confident identifying coins and notes, they need to spend time applying this knowledge. Open problems such as 'How many ways?' questions are a great way to stretch and push all of the children in your class. This is a low-threshold, high-ceiling task as there are different ways to develop it.

To begin with, choose an amount between 21 and 99p so that there is plenty of scope for multiple ways to make up the total with coins, such as 57p or 82p.

Ask the children to make the amount using coins. There might be different ways to make it. For example, with 57p you might have 50 + 5 + 2, or 20 + 20 + 10 + 5 + 2, or something different. Embrace and celebrate all the different ways around the class and make a note of them on the working wall or whiteboard.

Next, tell them you want to know how many different ways they can find to make the amount you have given them. You and any other adults in the room should circulate and see what kind of methods are being used around the classroom. Some children might go through in a systematic way, while others will have a more random approach.

At the end, collect in the different ways that they have used and see how many the children have come up with as a class.

Setting up shop!

'There is no better way to teach children about calculating and giving change. Turn your classroom into a shopping centre!'

This idea gives your pupils time to practise everything that they have learnt after you have spent time teaching the different coins, how to make different quantities using coins and how we calculate change.

Use objects from around the school to set up a supermarket, a book shop, a cuddly toy shop and any other shop you can think of. Try to get at least five shops so the children can spread out between them.

Label up the items with differing price tags ranging from small amounts like 10p to larger prices such as £3.59 but nothing more than £4.99. Each child will have a £10 note to spend in the shops (this could be increased for older children).

Each child will take it in turns to be a shopkeeper and a customer. The shopkeepers will need to calculate and give the correct change. The customers need to use their fake money to buy different items, and ensure their change is correct.

Give them time to browse the items on sale and let them wander around buying the items that they want. The teacher and any additional adults in the room should focus on watching the children giving accurate change and ensuring that they are using the different strategies that you have been through in class. Some children might need more support when giving change so could be paired up with an adult or a more able pupil to support them.

Teaching tip

Some children will whizz through this activity with their eyes closed so set them the challenge of spending as much of their £10 on as many different items as possible.

Budgeting for your break!

'Putting money into this kind of real-life situation means the children will need to think carefully about budgeting.'

This idea is all about budgeting. It can be adapted and developed for different year groups but works well from Year 4 up.

This can be done independently or in pairs/ groups and should have a competitive aspect to push the class to do well. You will need to give the class a scenario to work with and different conditions and rules to work to.

For example, you might tell the class that they are planning a camping holiday for a family of four. They will be in charge of choosing the travel, accommodation, food and activities. Set them a budget, e.g. £500, and explain that going over budget will disqualify them from the competition.

Provide them with a sheet to write down and price up their final decisions.

You will need to give them priced-up options for each of the following:

- vehicle and petrol costs
- accommodation costs
- food packages
- excursion or activity packages
- camping equipment.

Tell the class that they have one hour to find the best camping holiday for the best price.